JILL AND THE HORSEMASTERS

Jill and the Horsemasters

JEMMA SPARK

CONTENTS

| 1 |

Chapter One – Alight with Ambition

I awoke one morning in June 1963, nearly twenty-years-old, alight with excitement and anticipation. Today was the day that I would ride my dream dressage horse, Skydiver. The plan was he would carry me to glory, Riding for England in the dressage competition in the Olympics. Well, that was the grand scheme. I hadn't actually been selected yet. In fact, I had only ever ridden in one dressage test but, I did have oodles of experience riding in small gymkhanas and local shows, and I'd even competed in a point-to-point! How hard could it be?

My immediate plan was to begin training and competing in dressage competitions around England, and perhaps even venturing over the Channel to compete in Europe. The long-term plan was the 1968 Mexico Olympics. Putting aside my sporadic attempts to study the German language, I might have to start learning Spanish.

For months, I had been trying to buy my dressage horse, Skydiver, and finally, I had pulled it off. How I had acquired him is detailed in my previous book *Jill Dreams of a Dressage Horse*. I don't want to give away the story for those of you who have not read this book, but suffice to say, it was not a straightforward purchase, but had been achieved through a series of adventures and misadventures. In the past, my dreams had been more modest, and had never stretched beyond competing in the open show jumping competition at Chatton Show, which is the village in which I grew up.

You need to understand that in 1963, in England, dressage was not exactly the Done Thing and was only just gaining popularity, probably in no small measure, due to the Pullein-Thompson sisters writing pony books that championed the cause. Let no-one underestimate the power of pony books. To some of us, they are quite definitely the Stuff of Life!

Skydiver was beautiful, rather like the horses I had ridden in Germany. A warmblood-type with some thoroughbred mixed in. He was not just the commonplace grey, his coat had an almost metallic sheen, and he had a luxuriant jet-black mane and tail with dark markings on his legs. His head was small, with a wide distance between liquid dark eyes fringed by black eyelashes that needed no mascara. His ears very neat and pointed, almost pixie ears, an elegant neck, perfectly sloped shoulders and, a peachy bottom – which is a wonderful feature on a horse. not so great for people!

I had only just done the deal to purchase him, with a somewhat dubious person called Tatiana de Vere, and brought him back from Essex, not yesterday but the day before. Yesterday had been Susan Pyke's wedding and, that grand event is also described in my previous book.

Moving on. Today I was to ride Skydiver, a schooling session which I had planned in excruciating detail, lying awake in the still watches of the night. The small area in my field where I had schooled my ponies during my youth was not particularly suitable for this. I had dreamed of floating along the ground in an extended trot. To achieve this, I needed space. So, I would ride down to Neshbury Common. Secretly, I rather liked the idea that we might attract an audience. I had that wonderful feeling when you want to shout to the world about your happiness and hope, that others might join in, cheering from the sidelines.

It was a perfect summer morning. Sunlight fell in golden swathes, and the road verges were shimmering with creamy-white Queen Anne's lace, offset by densely green hedgerows. The way to Neshbury Common led past a succession of little cottages wreathed with flowering creepers, a riotous combination of oranges, yellows, reds, and pinks. From high up on Skydiver's back, I could glimpse the fields in the distance, standing grass shivering and rippling in the breeze.

Skydiver was a divine horse. His stride was long and straight, and he held the bit in his mouth delicately. When Tatiana had owned him, he had been stabled twenty-four hours a day and only exercised in arenas, until called upon to perform on a film set. I thought that he might enjoy some dollops of fresh air in the glorious outdoors. I wondered if perhaps he was a little too perfect, whether the strain of always doing the right thing might one day overwhelm him and end in disaster. But this was too gloomy a thought for such a morning of bright hope. I returned to surfing my wave of happiness.

There were a few people on the far side of the Common walking their dogs, but I had a large flat area to myself. I began to circle at the rising trot. Then I sat down and tried a sitting trot. This was not one of my best subjects. However, on Skydiver it was more comfortable than any horse I had ever ridden. I pushed him on so that he used more impulsion and kind of compressed himself, bringing his hindquarters beneath his body and bending his head at the poll, that is the top of his head.

I gave him the aid to progress to an extended trot, and it was then that I felt pure elation. He flung his feet out, pointing his toes as if he were a ballerina. We literally floated across the luxuriant grass that grew on the Common in the summer. I wished then that my old enemy, Susan Pyke would happen by and see me riding my new horse. She would be pea-green with envy. But the two of us were no longer competing on the same level.

She would be on her honeymoon today, enjoying her first day as Mrs Bartholomew King – what a mouthful! Susan's husband appeared to my jaundiced eye to be an incredibly boring man, a mere solicitor – the dullest and dreariest swain in the local muddy pool of young-to-middle-aged men. The happy couple, no doubt oozing conjugal bliss, were to move into a new house built in an upmarket housing development in Rychester, our nearby town. Susan was aiming to become one of those 'ladies that lunch'. To me, this was utter anathema. I would rather be a gipsy living in a caravan on the edge of the moor, or an exotic socialite who summered in the south of France, before I married a dull-as-ditch-water, middle-class professional man and lived in a housing estate in Rychester!

It had been fun seeing lots of our old friends at the wedding, and I had had a tremendous stroke of luck if only I could pull it off. April Cholly-Sawcutt had suggested that I contact the assistant to the Deputy Editor of *Horse and Hound* regarding me writing articles about dressage. This had quite literally Fallen in My Lap as I had thought about the possibility of being a journalist, and that meant, of course, a journalist who wrote about horsey subjects and dressage, in particular, was my Big New Thing.

I would phone the assistant to the Deputy Editor straight after lunch. Now I wanted to concentrate on riding my amazing new horse. It would have been better if I could have taken him to Linda McNally's so she could train us. She had a riding school down the road from Blainstock Castle in Scotland, where my mother, stepfather, and brand-new baby brother, Hamish, lived. It was Linda who had introduced me to the fine art of dressage riding and who had suggested that I go to Germany to get some training. She was a brilliant rider. I had tremendous respect for her. But I wasn't planning on going back to Scotland until early August, just after Chatton Show.

The paying guests who stayed at the castle for the grouse shooting season would arrive before the Glorious Twelfth when the season began. I had at least seven weeks ahead of me. I had not only my beautiful new dressage horse but also Balius, my thoroughbred with a dash of Highland pony blood, to ride in the local showjumping competitions.

I continued riding, now cantering in elegant circles, and I found that my new horse was utterly faultless. I wondered who had trained him. It surely wasn't the people at De Luxe Movie Horses from whom I had bought him. I thought perhaps it might have been Henry Wynmalen who was probably the top horseman in England at this time. I wondered if I should write to him and send him a photo and ask if he knew anything about Skydiver's background. This cunning plan might just result in him asking us to stay so he could train us, in the same way, that he had invited the Pullein-Thompson sisters and Sheila Willcox, the current glamour girl of the eventing scene.

We cantered a full circle, and then I turned up a straight line. I had done four tempi changes on Skydiver when I had first ridden him a few months ago. This time I asked for two tempi changes. That is when a horse changes his or her leading leg at the canter every two strides. I was struck with the thought that Skydiver was just too good for me. I wondered if I was going to mess it up. I have described how I had used to make these fancy moves with Black Boy in one of my original books, *Jill and the perfect pony.*

When I got home and put him back in his loose box, the phone rang. It was Tatiana de Vere, the woman who ran the Movie Horse company. She wanted to arrange to come and pick up Copperplate and her colt. This had been the deal, a part-exchange of Copperplate's colt for Skydiver. Copperplate was to go and stay in Essex at Tatiana's stables until the colt was weaned, then I would get her back.

It would certainly make it easier to juggle the horses at Pool Cottage. I had Balius and Skydiver, and Ann, my best friend, who lived in the cottage with me, had my former steeplechaser, Black Comedy. During the day, Black Comedy went down to Ann's parents' house to stay in the field, but then we brought him back at night. There were only two loose boxes and four horses and one foal. Now that I was the proud owner of Pool Cottage, I might perhaps build another loose box, but the expense would be huge. I wasn't sure that I would stay at Chatton for any length of time. I was regularly shuttling between Blainstock Castle and Oxfordshire.

I made myself a cup of tea and a sandwich before I rang the woman at *Horse and Hound*. Her name was Beatrice Garter. I gave myself a good talking to. This could be the cataclysmic breakthrough in my career as a journalist. I had a proven background in writing books as I had authored my own series of autobiographical pony books. But writing as a journalist was another field of endeavour and would require quite a different technique. Although, if April Cholly-Sawcutt had been contracted to write about showjumping, how hard could it be? I wondered how much was talent and how much the pony club-old tie brigade. Her father was Captain Cholly-Sawcutt, who had represented Britain as a showjumper for many years. Unfortunately, he had Alzheimer's now and hardly recognised his family members.

I took five deep breaths and dialled the number. Beatrice Garter answered the phone, and I told her my name and that April had suggested I ring her. She sounded distracted and disinterested. My spirits flopped down through my boots. I was going to have to sell myself. She suggested we have a meeting but couldn't fit me in for another two weeks, and could I bring in something I'd written, some sort of article between 800 and 1200 words. It didn't have to be about dressage, but something entertaining, suitable for *Horse and Hound*.

We made the appointment, and I sat down. I found myself shaking. I had to write an article. I needed something that was going to blow her socks off. I could have been supremely egotistical and written a review of my pony book series, but I decided that just wouldn't do. Sometimes I had a sneaky suspicion that my pony books are indeed what one could call an 'ecstasy of self-indulgence'. Although of late, I've touched on gritty reality, I soon veer back to what my reviewers have called a representation of Arcadian bliss. Now I needed a story – something entertaining certainly, but also something real, not just another flight of fancy!

I decided to take Balius out for a ride, thinking that the best inspiration comes when one is on horseback, looking at the world through the ears of a horse. And if I were going to take him to some shows in the next few months, then I needed to sharpen him up a bit. Just recently, I'd been caught up in the filming of Macbeth at the castle. Balius had been left on the sidelines. We headed up to Mrs Darcy's riding school, which my good friend, Wendy Mead, had been running for several years. In the ordinary course of things, I would have been straight up there with Skydiver to show off my new horse but, the situation had changed and, I didn't feel entirely comfortable there anymore.

Off and on over the years, I had worked for Mrs Darcy and Wendy, but they had recently hired a new instructor called Serena. Now I was no longer needed. The worst of this was that she was 'qualified', whereas I was not. This rankled, I can tell you. She had the BHS Preliminary Instructor's Certificate, which was recognised throughout the horse world.

This, in conjunction with the fact that Ann had gone back to school to get into Veterinary College and Dinah Dean was studying law at Cambridge, really drove it home to me that I wasn't qualified as anything. I had a ragbag collection of skills such as typing a bit, slow and laborious shorthand, some very rudimentary German language knowledge, and teaching horse riding, but only at a very low level. I had the sense that everyone was forging on with their lives. I was being left behind. It made me feel cold and empty. Then it struck me that one of the consequences of writing autobiographical books was that I had started living my life as if I were a character in a novel, thinking constantly about myself, chewing and, worrying over it as if I were a cat at its dinner.

I rode Balius up to the riding school, hoping to talk to Wendy. Serena was in the arena teaching some of the Rychester housewives that came up now for regular classes. I told Wendy about my new dressage horse. She was pleased for me, but I could see she was distracted. She had a class of young students coming this afternoon and needed to get the ponies in and saddle them up.

I rode Balius up to the back paddock and cantered him around the cross-country course a couple of times. Then, to my horror, I saw Serena standing by the fence watching me! My feelings about Serena were at best described as ambivalent, but in fact, my Noble Self was being drowned in a flood of envy. I felt very huffy. It didn't help that she had longer legs than me. This wasn't envy that she might be more attractive, but that long legs were good for riders as they can wrap them around a horse and had less chance of falling off. When I was a child and wanted longer legs, I had considered hanging on the washing line with weights on my feet, to see if I could stretch my lower limbs.

Now I have to be fair-minded. It was not Serena's fault that nature had blessed her with long legs. And the fact that she had gained her Certificate was all to her credit. She had done absolutely nothing wrong. I had swanned down to the riding school whenever it suited me and picked up a bit of casual work, but when something better beckoned, I was off again. She had been hired full-time, been committed, and now had totally made a success of it! I had even lowered myself to have a lesson with her a few months ago, and although not as brilliant a teacher as Linda, she was sound. There was nothing in her that couldn't be admired, but although I rummaged to the bottom of my soul for some decency, I found only envy and outraged pride.

I pulled up and walked over to her, trying to look at least a little friendly.

"Hello, Jill," she called. "He's looking good!"

"Yes, he's been a bit neglected lately. I've just bought a new horse, a trained dressage horse!"

I was utterly appalled that comment had slipped from my lips. I sounded just like the boastful Susan Pyke, who was always skiting about her newest horse. She had had a long line of 'new horses' all discarded and replaced when she hadn't been able to ride them. What was I becoming!

My face went scarlet with embarrassment and humiliation. I felt myself glowing like a beetroot!

"How exciting!" said the saintly and serene Serena. There didn't seem an ounce of envy or malice in her. "You must bring him up. I would love to see him."

Then I realised she wanted to be friends. There was nothing but admirable qualities in this rival? It made me feel lower than the lowest worm. I opened my mouth, but nothing came out. My Ignoble Nature had cornered me.

"How are you?" I managed to mutter.

She laughed lightly, a delicate tinkle that ran up and down like a musical scale.

"I love this job, the most delightful students, and Chatton is such a friendly village," she replied.

"Did you hear that Susan Pyke was married yesterday?" I asked, then could have kicked myself. It was as if I were taunting her because she had not been invited.

"Yes, Wendy told me all about it. And you caught the bouquet!" She smiled at me merrily.

Bingo! She'd got me one. Wham! I hated the idea of having to find myself a husband one day. Catching the bouquet had been the absolute end, mitigated only by the fact that Susan had fallen over with her legs in the air, as her Cinderella horse and carriage had run away without their driver, just after she'd flung the bridal bouquet into the air.

"Yes," I muttered. "Anyway, I better head off home."

Serena obligingly opened the gate for me and waved me off in a friendly fashion. All the way home I muttered to myself. I knew exactly what Mummy would say, and she would have been absolutely right, but I just couldn't seem to find a skerrick of goodwill in my paltry soul. I turned my mind away from the Serena issue. I needed to think about the article that I had to produce, like a cat out of a hat, to secure a job with *Horse and Hound*. My life had gone beyond the bounds of Chatton. I had to find success in the wider world. I had to prove my worth!

Ann was at Pool Cottage when I got back.

"Jill, did you ride that darling new horse of yours? I wish I'd been here to see it!" She was all sweetness and light. This made me feel even grumpier.

"Yes, I took him up to the Common and did a bit of schooling. He behaved perfectly," I replied, scowling.

She gave me an odd look but didn't comment. She probably thought I was becoming a moody old maid!

"I've got the morning off tomorrow, so I'd love to see how he goes?" she said.

"Yes, yes, and you must have a ride on him," I insisted. At least my Better Self triumphed when it came to Ann who had always been my most stalwart supporter.

"Would you let me ride him?" she asked hesitantly. "Are you sure you think I'm good enough?"

"Of course, you are," I said firmly. "But there's something else you might be able to help me with, as I'm clueless, and I've got to come up with something stupendous!"

"Tell! Tell!" she said cheerfully. She untacked Balius after I dismounted, and together we rubbed him down. There was the usual dilemma of which horse went in the field, as we were short two loose boxes.

"That Tatiana de Vere is turning up sometime tomorrow to pick up Copperplate and her colt," I said. Then I remembered how upset Ann had been to hear that I had sold the foal and looked over at her anxiously.

"It's alright. I've come to terms with it," she said lightly, knowing what I was thinking. "At least this shuffling them around will be more manageable. So, Copperplate and Skydiver in the loose boxes tonight and Balius in the field with Black Comedy. It's so warm I'm sure they'll be much happier out under the stars."

We went inside, and Ann had already prepared a delicious stew or more probably picked it up from her mother's. It was warming in the oven. As we ate, I told her about my telephone conversation with Beatrice Garter and how I had to write an entertaining horsey article to prove my journalistic ability.

"It's actually much harder when you have to think of a topic," mused Ann. "It would have been easier if they'd given you a definite subject."

"I know," I groaned. "It's like at school, when the English mistress said write about anything, and of course, it's hard to think of one single thing."

"I'll give it some thought," said Ann looking into the middle distance with an intelligent expression.

"Thank goodness, I've got you," I said.

"Don't be silly Jill, now don't you go getting all maudlin and sentimental on me. You're not like this because of Susan and Barty King surely!"

I laughed out loud at this. Then I confessed to my feelings about the Saintly Serena.

"I can understand that, but she is a decent girl, and it's not her fault that she was employed by Wendy."

"I know, I've been an absolute beast over it. I swanned in when it suited me and expected a bit of work here and there. That was hardly fair on Wendy. She needed proper commitment, someone who put the riding school first. But what about Serena being qualified? I think that is what rubs me up the wrong way so much."

"Oh, Jill! You lead a charmed life. Blainstock Castle in the Highlands with every equestrian facility known to man. Your own cottage in Oxfordshire with a field and two loose boxes. Not to mention a horse box, the use of a Land Rover, and a two-horse trailer."

I hung my head in shame.

"And charm, good looks, and intelligence!" she added, really rubbing it in.

"Alright. Alright. I'm going to count my blessings," I muttered.

| 2 |

Chapter Two - The Clattering Clutterbucks

The next evening Ann came back from college looking very smug as if she knew some tremendous secret.

"Tell! Tell! I know that look!" I cried, once again afraid that she was going to tell me she was engaged to Henry, her boyfriend, the vet.

She began to talk, in a sing-song roundabout sort of way of old men telling a long and involved tale, and I had to bite my tongue, to stop myself snapping at her to get to the point. The long and the short of it was she had rung up Tartine, who lives in London, who had come up with the most amusing and quirky story for me to write about. I grimaced faintly. I had never met Tartine, but she was a very posh French woman, who Ann had known in her days living in Paris, walking out with Pierre the Rat, who had thrown her over for an older married woman. I had never really liked the sound of Tartine, but that's probably my Awful Jealous Nature surfacing again, as it seemed to do quite regularly these days.

"Tartine was telling me quite the most amusing story, and then it came to me! Wallop! This was going to be absolutely perfect for you, Jill, and there's a great photo in it too!" enthused Ann.

"What?" I shouted at her.

"There's a house, quite near South Kensington and Tartine was trit-trotting past on her high shoes, which I have to say, you absolutely never see her in anything else, she says a woman can't be seen dead in flat shoes."

Inwardly I grimaced at this piece of horrid flummery. I kept my mouth straight and lowered my eyelids, so my eyes didn't flash disdain-fully. Personally, I hated high heels they had to be the most uncomfort-able shoes ever invented by men, to torture women into a shape that men alone would find pleasing.

"As I was saying, she was near one of those terraced houses in the back streets and out the front door came two ponies, saddled up and led by two girls, who mounted them on the street and walked off down the road. They came out the front door!"

"How strange," I mused. "The front door you say, that is unusual, you know you might be right, I don't suppose you've got the address."

"I certainly have," said Ann smugly. "And I thought you could bor-row that new super-duper camera that Mummy and Daddy gave me for my birthday. I'll have to show you how to use it with all the buttons and bows on it, but it does take very good photographs."

"That would be kind," I replied. "I don't suppose you could come with me and take photos and be my assistant?"

Ann laughed at me.

"Jill, I've never known you bashful like that!"

"It's just, I'm not sure I'd get the camera thing right, and I don't want to mess it up!" I exclaimed defensively. "I wonder where they keep the horses? Do you think they're in the living room and eat at the dining room table *en famille*?"

"Possibly," said Ann carefully, as if dealing with someone on the out-skirts of looney land. "But I imagine that they keep them in the back garden, in stables, and they have no rear gate."

"Yes, yes, of course. That's what I was thinking. Have you got the address?"

"Of course, here it is, I've written it down for you," said Ann. "I could come with you the day after tomorrow, as I've got lunch lined up with Henry."

I was about to snap her head off, that a mere lunch with Henry was more important than my journalistic career, but then stopped myself. I wondered how I could have become so self-centred, or perhaps I'd always been that way and just never noticed before.

I made plans for the next two days. I wanted to try Skydiver in a proper arena and thought I might take him round to visit Lavender Ellison-Heath; the young girl who now owned Black Boy, my first pony. She was a very decent type, even if she had renamed Black Boy as Bingle Jells. I had to forgive her this rather bizarre aberration, her mother was an absolute horror, and it might well have caused some deep-seated strange twisting in poor Lavender's psyche.

I rang the Ellison-Heath residence and talked to the dreaded Mrs E-H. She was her usual ghastly self, all strangled vowels, and little pauses as she desperately calculated the 'correct answer' to my social questions. I had never known anyone more pretentious and less successful at carrying it off. Poor Lavender must cringe every time her mother opened her mouth.

We arranged that I should go over the following morning, and Mrs E-H insisted that I stay for lunch and tell her all about the exciting Macbeth filming at the castle. I hoped desperately that she hadn't seen that photo of Lady Macbeth trying to strangle a local girl that had appeared in a newspaper – the 'local girl' had been me, but my face was so contorted with being strangled, that I hoped no-one had recognised me!

I rose early the following morning. The sky was a crystalline blue with white billowing clouds like feather beds. I was determined to make the most of this fantabulous weather. I loved the beginning of summer with the prospect of horse shows, banter, camaraderie, and old rivalries resurrected.

Lavender had a fantastic schooling area, forty yards by sixty yards, the same size as two dressage arenas put side by side. Ann and I would have died and gone to heaven to have had such an arena, when we were young and had built our showjumps out of bits and pieces, including cardboard boxes.

Lavender was thrilled to see me, which was gratifying. My poor, old, battered ego seemed to need constant stroking these days. I wondered if I was developing an inferiority complex as a sort of approaching middle-age crisis. Although at nineteen, twenty this November, I didn't think that I was exactly middle-aged.

Lavender was enthralled with Skydiver and rushed me down to the arena, leaping up and down, asking me to show her what he could do. I trotted and then cantered around. Then I set him off with the beginning of some lateral work – that is going sideways.

In Germany, I had learned that you do leg yielding at the walk, and shoulder-in at the trot, as you need a more active pace, so I began with shoulder-in. It's a good exercise and is used in more advanced tests. It needs flexion from three major hind leg joints. Although it is sideways, it helps to keep your horse straight.

Lavender watched intently. Then I faced a deluge of questions from her regarding the movement. I suggested she go and saddle up Bingle, and she could try it herself. Thus, we spent an hour together. Skydiver did everything I asked of him. Finally, I attempted one-tempi changes at the canter, and he did it perfectly. I was so happy I had this curious topped-up feeling, that can be fatal. It is as if the world is your oyster, and I felt myself becoming flippant to the point of utterly flipping out. Dancing on air is a very curious type of exultation. I seemed to be zooming up and down the scale of feelings; from deepest gloom at being replaced by Serena, to my dreams of winning gold medals at the Olympics.

I called a halt to our schooling session as I didn't want to overdo it. We untacked and rubbed down the horses and went into lunch. Lavender had to go and change, and I scrubbed up as best I could in the bathroom, which was decorated in a rather ghastly shade of mauve.

All the interior decoration in this house was horrible. It had once been a home of small, delightfully proportioned rooms which had suffered being knocked through to create larger rooms which featured the latest modern contraptions such as a cumbersome television set, two artificial log fires, and the most hideous cocktail cabinet in the drawing-room. We went through into a narrow, rather dark dining-room and were served lunch by a maid wearing a stiff black and white uniform, which rustled in a particularly creepy way. Undoubtedly, this was Mrs E-H's idea of posh. The food was dreadful. Cold lettuce soup with a thin, miserable dribble of cream in a snail-pattern, and tiny hard bread rolls with curls of butter, followed by a very sad, wilted salad with small cubes of chicken that seemed more plastic than flesh, hard walnuts and shrivelled sultanas. I ploughed through the revolting repast with as much polite enthusiasm as I could garner.

Mrs E-H babbled on, her strangled vowels massacred the English language, and she waved around her hands that looked like little claws, with mauve-painted talons for fingertips.

"Dear Lavender has learned *so* much from Serena," she told me, smiling fondly. I wondered if she was deliberately trying to tell me that Serena was a better teacher than myself. I ground my teeth with anguish, determined not to show her how this line of conversation was so annoying. Lavender bravely broke into this stream of praise for the perfect Serena, telling her mother about Skydiver and how amazing he was. This led to an even worse string of ideas from her maddening mother.

"I was thinking that dear Bingle is just not the thing for Lavender now, I think we should find her a top-quality show pony, something that will get her to Harringay, to the very top, you know!" Lavender's face went white, obviously aghast at this idea.

"No, Bingle is perfect for me, at this stage," she said. "You know we're planning all these shows and gymkhanas this summer, while I'm still in the 12-years-and-under classes. It would be the worst thing, to appear on a top show pony, when I've no experience at all of showing and riding classes. It would be just so *nouveau riche!*"

Clever little Lavender. This was a sensitive point for her mother as *nouveau riche* just about nailed it when it came to the Ellison-Heaths. I jumped in to help her.

"I did rather well locally with Bingle. All the local judges know him, and he was usually very highly-placed," I said, trying to find the best angle to make my point.

"The judges know him," said Mrs E-H, thinking about this. It must have pleased her because she stopped talking about buying a beautiful show pony. I thought perhaps we had brought about a stay of execution. At that point, I should have told her that if they were to sell Bingle, then I would like to buy him back. But for today, Bingle was safe with Lavender, who loved him dearly.

"Are you going to buy some form of horse transport, to get around the shows?" I asked, thinking that the logistics of buying a Land Rover and trailer, or a small horse box could occupy Mrs E-H's acquisitive nature for a while.

"Yes, you're right, I must look into it, I will find us a grand little truck, with all the modern conveniences," she said as if inspired, imagining what a fine dash they would cut in the local equestrian world.

"So, do tell us, Jill, where did you find this amazing dressage horse?" There was a hard edge to her voice.

"He was one of the horses used in the film, and he belonged to a rather exclusive stable in Colchester, and they accepted an offer," I replied. "Of course, they didn't want to sell him, but I pushed very hard. I just had to have him."

I knew that anything I told her would get straight back to her goddaughter, Susan King née Pyke, so I was careful what I said. I didn't want Susan spreading it round that I had bought a performing circus horse!

After lunch, Lavender came with me around to the stables and helped me to saddle up Skydiver. I rode home down the road and thought that perhaps Skydiver was beginning to relax and enjoy his new existence with all these excursions into the summer countryside. Perfect horse heaven!

I got back to Pool Cottage just in time for Tatiana de Vere's arrival. She roared up the driveway in an enormous, juggernaut horse box, with 'De Luxe Movie Horses' emblazoned across the side of it in a fiery red-orange script. Leaping down from the cab, she strode towards me. I had to steel myself not to step back at her determined advance. This was a woman to be reckoned with! She was tall, statuesque, a Valkyrie with an arrogant air that was truly terrifying.

I called Copperplate up to the gate, and I slipped a halter over her head and led her forward. Her little golden colt cavorted around her. Tatiana took the lead rope and led Copperplate straight into the horse box. The colt skittered and teetered at the base of the ramp, anxiously watching his mother disappear into the bowels of the truck. It wasn't the way I would have done it. He'd already been taught to lead, and if I'd got a halter on him, we could have led him straight up behind his mother. Blast Tatiana with her arrogant impatience!

I walked up to him and put my arm under his neck, my other hand on his nose. I gently encouraged him to go up the ramp. He neighed shrilly to his mother, who knickered back in a deep, gentle voice.

"Come on, little man, follow your mother," I crooned to him.

Tatiana snorted above us. I wondered if she wasn't half-horse herself, which is an insult to all horses. The colt was driven by a desperate desire to stay with his mother, and he bounded up the ramp. His exuberant leap pushed me aside, and I was grovelling on the tail ramp, looking like an absolute fool. Again, Tatiana snorted at me and promptly shut the colt in with his mother.

"Get up!" she commanded me as she jumped down and started to crank up the ramp. Once I was back on the ground, I gathered up whatever scraps of dignity I retained, noticing that my knees had manure stains all over them.

"I'll come and pick her up before Christmas," I said firmly, looking Tatiana in the eye. When I had purchased Skydiver, she had tried to palm another horse off on me, and I knew I had to be very careful with her.

"Good-bye," she barked at me and jumped into the cab and reversed down the driveway at speed and spun out into the road. I was left standing in a black cloud of diesel fumes that made me feel like retching. I had a horrible empty feeling inside and desperately hoped that I had done the right thing letting Copperplate go with her. Although, I had to admit that everything was much easier now that we had only three horses to juggle around.

The next morning, after Ann had taken Black Comedy down to the Derry's field going on to meet Henry for lunch at a pub in Oxford, I put Skydiver in the field, and brought in Balius. I thought that I might take him for a long hack up beyond Neshbury Common down to the river.

We trotted along the grass verges, and I felt like singing out loud. I began to dream of the future this summer. I would take Balius in the open jumping at Chatton Show and Skydiver in the riding and hack classes. I had some rather smart new riding clothes that I had purchased in Germany. I was swinging back to my topped-up exultant state. I began to plan my life. I would trawl through the local paper and *Horse and Hound* and make a plan of which events to enter. I would try and find a dressage competition, but I knew that they were few and far between. I would not even entertain the thought of entering him in one-day events as I didn't want to risk his precious legs, especially around a cross-country course. I was firmly set on riding him only in dressage.

With Balius, it was another story. His dressage was coming along, but he was better at jumping, and he had the toughness of a Highland pony, which made me feel safe around cross-country courses. But if I were to ride him across country, then he needed to get fitter. I found a long slow hill, and we set off cantering slowly. I leaned forward and let the wind whistle past my face. They say that riding a horse is like borrowing freedom, and that is what it felt like.

Ann and I set off to London the following morning in our quest to find the 'ponies who came through the front door'. I wasn't sure what budding journalists wore, and I didn't automatically reach for my jodhpurs on every occasion these days. Finally, I chose some rather smart slacks and a plain shirt with a discreet gold chain necklace that Mummy had given me on my eighteenth birthday.

"I've got the camera with two rolls of film, and the address, and I assume you've got your notebook," said Ann cheerily as we rolled down the road to London. "This is going to be a hoot! I do love going on adventures with you, Jill!"

It was another topping day. All the summer stretched before us, whispering promises of joy! There were swaying elms on both sides of the road. They seemed to be paying homage to our quest.

"Let's hope the ponies are home and haven't gone on holiday to their summer cottage," said Ann light-heartedly. This was a horrible thought. I had no idea what to do for a story if they weren't there. For once, I felt empty of new ideas. Usually, they were bursting out of my brain.

Ann wove her way down through London, expertly passing cars and nipping across lanes to get ahead. We made it into leafy Kensington in a remarkably short time. We found a parking spot within sight of the door from which the ponies were reported to emerge. It was quiet. No-one coming and going. I felt like we were secret agents spying on our targets.

"Are we going to knock?" asked Ann.

"Do you think they'll want to tell us their story?" I ask doubtfully. I wasn't too keen on getting into the news myself. "Let's just wait here for a while."

"On the other hand, if you take a photo without asking permission, then they're less likely to want to talk to you," reasoned Ann.

We sat there for several minutes in silence.

"Let's go! We'll knock on the door. There may not even be anyone home," I said, my impatience overtaking my nervousness.

We knocked. It was a green door with a white stripe painted around it. I was so hyped up I noticed tiny inconsequential details. I could hear my heart beating inside my chest. I told myself this was ridiculous. If I couldn't doorknock for a small story, how would I go with the big scoop?

No-one answered. We waited. I knocked again. We were about to turn away, and I heard footsteps. A diminutive blonde girl answered.

"I'm sorry. I was out the back with the ponies," she said, smiling at us. "Can I help you?"

I knew then that we were at the right address. She had ponies out the back. Now it was simply a matter of charming her. I wondered if I shouldn't have worn my riding clothes, to show that I was a horsey person.

"Hello, I'm Jill Crewe, and this is my friend Ann Derry," I said, thrusting my hand out towards her. Tentatively she took my hand and shook it.

"I'm Pat Clutterbuck," she replied.

"What a gorgeous name!" I exclaimed, thinking this would embellish the story with a small curious detail. "I'm a writer, and I'm on the trail of a fascinating little story. Someone told me that you bring your horses out the front door," I said, smiling.

"What would you write about that?" she asked, seeming genuinely puzzled.

"It is rather unusual to bring your horses out through the front door," I explained. "You keep them in your back garden?"

"Yes, that's right. My sister Ellie has one, and I have another, and we've no back gate," she explained.

"I'm going for a job at *Horse and Hound,* and I've got to write an article to show them that I'm up to it. I wondered if I could interview you and take a few photos?" I asked trying but failing, to suppress the pleading note in my voice.

"Jill Crewe?" she said slowly. "I've heard that name. You write the Jill books!"

"Yes, that's right, but I'm trying to branch out into journalism."

"Oh, wow! Ellie will be so excited. We adore your books! They're fab! We would love you to write about us," she fluttered.

I exhaled. It was as if I had been holding my breath for quite ten minutes.

"Do come in, I shouldn't be leaving you on the doorstep. Would you like some coffee?"

"Oh yes, please," said Ann, stepping over the threshold. "I knew this would all work out. Clever Tartine!"

"Yes, clever Tartine!" I agreed.

"Who is Tartine?" asked Pat.

"The friend who spotted you with the ponies coming out the door. She's the one who put us onto this," said Ann.

We sat down in a friendly sitting room. There were photos of ponies, and dogs, and relatives all smiling and looking jolly.

"Now, do tell! How do you manage it, keeping ponies in Central London?" I asked. "Do you mind if I take notes?"

"Not at all," she said.

"Where do you ride?" I asked.

"We go up Ken High Street and along Hyde Park and down Rotten Row, of course."

"Naturally," I said, making notes frantically.

"It's wonderful fun, we have friends all along the way, and there are other horses in London, you know, the mounted police and people like that."

I began to see the article taking shape: the Clutterbucks and all the other horses and riders in Central London. We could follow them along their route and describe the friends they met along the way.

"Would you mind if we came along with you and took photos and details of some of your buddies?"

"I know Ellie would love it! We usually go out in the afternoon. We attend this funny little school down the road, a private school which gives us the afternoons free. Mummy knows the headmistress. I've got the day off as I wasn't feeling too well this morning." She grinned at us.

"I guess school isn't your favourite thing," I smiled at her.

"How did you guess? But it's not so bad. They've got this curriculum that concentrates on the arts, poetry, literature, and Latin – they're not so keen on maths and algebra. It could be a lot worse!"

"Can we see the ponies?" asked Ann, "perhaps take a few photos of them in their stables in the back garden."

We had a great time meeting the ponies, and Ann leapt about snapping away with her fancy camera. I made copious notes. Ellie came home from school, and she and Pat could have been twins, although Pat was a little smaller. The ponies were also a lovely pair of light chestnuts with flaxen manes and tails. The four of them made a charming picture, trotting down the busy roads of London. By the time we had progressed with them, following in the car with me leaping out to snap away when they met their horsey friends, I had enough material to write a novel. It was going to be hard to keep it down to about 1,000 words.

"That was fun!" exclaimed Ann on the way home.

"I don't envy them the life," I said. "Chatton and Scotland are much better for riding."

"Oh definitely," said Ann, "but think of all those London children who might take hope that somehow they can get to ride, without having to live in the country."

"Wouldn't it be awful to have to live in a big city?" I mused. "There's something so wholesome and heavenly about the country."

"On the other hand, I have to admit I did rather like Paris. It was so romantic, and you could sit in these little cafes and watch the glamorous Parisians pass by."

I took the films into the chemist at Rychester and went home to start writing. I wrote, and I wrote, and my piece got bigger and bigger, and I knew that I just wasn't mastering the art. I wondered then about Hetty, who had written the Macbeth story. I hadn't seen her or talked to her since the whole Lady Macbeth debacle. It had been her that had first suggested that I turn to journalism. I didn't want to talk to her, as what we had done to Hermione Elliot had left a nasty taste in my mouth. Although, in the end, it had all turned out alright. Now, I could do with some help and, Hetty was a very experienced journalist. As far as I could see, she did rather owe me one.

I took Balius out again to try and think. I was determined to give him some fast work to get him as fit as possible. There was a one-day event in four weeks at Houghton Heath, and I was hoping that we could be ready for it. In truth, it was just a tinpot affair, as proper horse trials were held in the spring and the autumn. But for practice, it was just the ticket. Four weeks was enough to get him fit enough to gallop around a cross-country course. I was even wondering if I might enter Skydiver, do the dressage, and then withdraw him from the event on some pretext. It would be a chance to do a dressage test with him. I would enter both horses,

I would also contact Hetty and show her my work and get her advice. It would be interesting to see if her story on Macbeth had helped her get out of boring Court reporting and up the journalistic career ladder.

I got home and pulled out the piece of paper with contact details that Hetty had given me. I rang the number and asked for Henrietta Silverthorne. I had thought it would take endless phone calls and dead ends, and I was rather discombobulated when I heard Hetty's voice on the end of the line about ten seconds later.

"Hello, this is Henrietta, how can I help you?" She sounded smooth as silk, quintessentially professional, and not at all like the Hetty with whom I had shared my turret bedroom for quite some time, as we had plotted to get her a scoop on the Horrible Hermione who had made my life hell.

"Hi Hetty, it's Jill!"

"Jill, how are you? What did you think of the story?"

She seemed to have that ability to pick up seamlessly where we had left off.

"I was relieved that you didn't name me!" I said. "Did they run it in America?"

"Yes, one movie magazine picked it up. Do you want some money for it?" she asked, with just a trace of sourness. As if I were someone who was always in it for the money!

"Not at all! I told you I didn't want any bonus from America!" I retorted. "But I did want to ask you a favour. You know how you suggested I write some articles? Well, I've got an interview with *Horse and Hound,* and I have to take in a piece I've written. I'm just desperate! It keeps turning into a novel. I wondered if you'd help me with it. Just a bit of guidance about how to make it more professional? And shorter!"

"I don't see why not," said Hetty.

"I could meet up with you in London, have a coffee, and if you'd just cast an eye . . ," I suggested.

"No worries. Tomorrow, if you like. Lunch at The Owl and The Pussycat in Covent Garden," she replied.

"It's on me," I said, and she didn't argue.

| 3 |

Chapter Three – Hard-Bitten Hetty

Meeting Hetty was another trip to London, but I didn't mind. I could take the photos as well and see if she could help me pick out the ones that were the most suitable. I had narrowed it down to twelve, but I knew that was far too many. I still couldn't think of a headline. It was harder than thinking of chapter names for my novels. I'd come up with dozens, and none of them catchy! I set to work again so that I could present Hetty with my very best work.

I didn't even bother to think about what I should wear when I was getting ready to catch the train to London. I was too intent on gathering up my reams of paper, numerous drafts and packets of photos. I stuffed everything into a brown leather satchel that Ann had been using for college and set off to catch the bus from Chatton to Rychester.

On the train, I went over and over my drafts, scratching out words here and there, and inserting other words. The more I worked on it, the worse it seemed to get. I'd never had these difficulties when writing my pony books. I hoped that Hetty would be able to help me, but somehow it seemed a lot to ask for an hour's advice to turn me into a professional journalist. Perhaps there was some sort of college course I could do. Getting qualified was something that kept preying on my mind.

I arrived at The Owl and The Pussycat half an hour early. The waitress took me to a table for two, and I ordered myself a large orange juice. It was fun meeting someone for a business lunch. It made me feel all grown-up. 'About time!' I can hear some of you shouting.

Hetty came in ten minutes late. I had begun to think that she was going to cry off. She was wearing a rather smart suit. Her hair was neatly coiffed, and she had bright red lipstick that matched her painted fingernails. She hadn't looked at all like that in Scotland. She had been rather inconspicuously dressed, with no makeup, and her hair dragged back in a bun. In that way, she had blended into the background very well, but then she had been undercover.

"Tell us, did you get some kind of promotion after the Hermione article?" I asked.

"It went down rather well. I *have* now got a promotion but not exactly what I wanted, up the ranks but more desk-bound than a roving reporter. I'm working as a sub-editor in the features department."

"What exactly does a sub-editor do?" I asked, suddenly conscious of my total ignorance of the world of journalism.

She smiled at me in a superior way.

"I take articles written by journalists, or perhaps things that have come in over the wire and decide what gets printed and what doesn't. I check the spelling and grammar and the facts and edit it down to make it better. It's a very important job. Often it leads to becoming an editor."

"So, you don't mind looking at what I've written," I said, thrusting one of my versions of the story at her.

She scanned it and looked thoughtful.

"You see, you have to write in the correct manner for the publication. You said *Horse and Hound*. I'm not familiar with that magazine. Have you read it, know what its style is?"

"Of course, I've read it numerous times. But perhaps not with that in mind, more for my own pleasure. It's my favourite publication."

"Another tenet of journalism that keeps you on track is 'facts, quotes and, anecdotes'. I like this piece. It's interesting - entertaining. You've got quotes from the girls and a couple from the people they meet when they ride. The facts are the place where the ponies are kept, and the route to Rotten Row. You could perhaps add in a few amusing stories that they've told you. You need to streamline it. It does read like a bit of a fairy tale. Do you mind if I work on it a bit?"

"No, of course not, that would help enormously."

She took a pencil out of her rather smart crocodile-skin bag and set to work, crossing out ruthlessly, whole paragraphs, then circling and putting arrows to other places and adding in a few words here and there. I handed her the photos that I thought were the best. She flicked through them rapidly, selected three of them: one of the ponies in the stables in the back garden, one of them coming out of the front door and another of them trotting down a busy street.

"These three are probably the best. You know you have to give them the negatives?"

"Yes, I had worked that out," I replied a little huffily. Although, such petty annoyance was overwhelmed by a rush of gratitude towards her for helping me.

"You're not going to go and steal my story, are you?" I asked, suddenly struck with an awful suspicion.

"Clutterbucks Clatter Through the Streets of London? No, it's alright. I told you before it was part of the journalists' code that we always protect our sources."

I looked at her with my mouth open and scribbled down this cleverly alliterative title.

"Thank you so much, Hetty! You're an absolute brick, and you were the one who gave me the idea in the first place. Do you think I'll ever be good enough?" I asked.

"With work, but you have to be more self-disciplined. You tend to indulge yourself with your fancies and your runaway emotions. You need to be more focused. Did you end up getting that horse you wanted?"

"Yes, I did actually," I replied.

"Good on you," she said. "Perhaps you will get there."

We ate our meal, and I found myself suddenly starving. I knew now that I could get the article up to scratch, and I would spend hours studying *Horse and Hound,* and practising writing in their style. It was all going to come out right, after all.

"Thank you so much, Hetty," I said after insisting that I pay for lunch.

"Do you mind if I take the receipt?" she said, slipping it into a side pocket in her handbag.

"You never miss a trick," I observed, not sure whether to admire her astuteness or condemn her for a form of petty deception. Obviously, she would claim expenses. "I never sent you that receipt for your bed and board at the castle," I said.

"Don't worry, I sorted it," she replied, smiling at me smugly. "Next time you're in London, we should meet up. I can introduce you to some of my colleagues if you like. You're going to be one of us."

"An exclusive group," I sighed rapturously, feeling as if the magic doors were opening for me.

She smiled again and left, walking briskly down the pavement. All my life, I would remember her ruthless professionalism, not precisely as a role model, but certainly, someone to admire.

I had several days to work on my writing, and I had to get Balius fit. The future was looking rather rosy, and I felt spifflicatingly happy. Ann would say that everything was 'blissikins'.

I looked over Hetty's corrections on the train on the way home, and I saw how her sharp mind had sifted through my words and found the core of things, cutting out the superfluous and flowery bits. One day I wanted to write like her!

I had five more days before my appointment with Beatrice Garter. I knew now that I could do it. I felt confident I'd be given a chance to prove myself. I sat back, and the fields flashed by, and I dreamed of my name in lights, 'Equestrian Journalist Extraordinaire'!

I got back in time to take Balius for a long trot through the lanes. I couldn't just gallop him every day. To build stamina and fitness, he needed long steady work as well as gallops. I decided to ride Skydiver in my small field. I had read somewhere recently that working in a smaller arena was good discipline and helped one to achieve more accuracy. We trotted and cantered circles. Hetty had said that I needed more self-discipline. I would self-discipline myself like mad! When Hetty had said this to me, I had taken her seriously. As opposed to when my head-mistress had given her abysmal little talks about 'disciplined thinking'. Then I had entirely scorned the idea and drifted off in my rosy-gold dream of ponies and gymkhanas.

The days sped by, and soon I was due to head back into London for my all-important and fateful meeting with Beatrice Garter. This time I felt I should go all out and wear something more business-like. I dragged out a natty little bracken-coloured suit that was one of Mummy's cast-offs. Ann, with her eye for clothes developed in Paris, had not been impressed but, I thought it made me look rather wor-thy. I didn't want to swan into the offices of *Horse and Hound* and give the impression of a clothes horse looking for a little job before I mar-ried up. I did add a jaunty little black tilt hat that Ann had produced last time I'd worn this suit into a meeting with my literary agent. These decisions about what to wear for which occasion were extremely com-plex. I wished I could live in my favourite jodhpurs as I had as a child. I just couldn't get interested in clothes the way that Ann did. I won-dered if there might be a training course for such things, but perhaps it is merely sartorial instinct, visited upon some but not all of us.

I placed the final-final draft of my article and the photos I'd chosen and the negatives in an envelope and stepped out down the road to Chatton, to get the bus to Rychester. I was very early, but I feared a hold-up. To arrive late on such an important day would be disastrous.

The train chuffed into London, and I caught a red double-decker bus to the magazine headquarters, an imposingly tall, brown-brick building. I entered and approached the grand polished wood reception desk and spoke to a woman who had the most fantastic beehive hair. It almost touched the ceiling! She sent me up the elevator to the sixth floor. I had expected Miss Beatrice Garter to be an august figure who I would approach with reverence, but whatever you expect, so often turns out to be the opposite. Behind the official façade of this magazine company, and I'm sure you know that *Horse and* Hound was first published in 1884, was a warren of dusty offices, interconnected and rambling down long corridors. I was almost overcome by the sight of groaning overloaded desks, dusty shelves with all sorts of intriguing ancient books on horse breeding, hound breeding, horse racing, and tomes of horse history that encompassed all aspects of our wonderful horse-riding tradition in Britain. Everywhere you looked were piles and piles of untidy paper.

Miss Garter was grey-haired with enormous owl-like glasses and a harassed expression. She looked at me blankly, as if I were a stranger from outer space.

"Good morning, I'm Jill Crewe, I've come to see you about writing articles on dressage," I said, hoping this would prompt her memory, which was probably overcrowded with far more important issues than my tiny and inconsequential self. She blinked at me like a small marsupial just woken from winter hibernation.

"Dressage, dressage, ..." she said vaguely, as if she had never heard of the concept. Admittedly many of the old guard in Britain were still sticking to the notion that it was new-fangled rubbish, but I had expected more from the workers in the vanguard of the equestrian movement in our great land.

"Oh, no!" Both her wrinkled, veiny old hands, marked with dark brown age-spots flew to her crinkled, dry cheeks. "I forgot! I forgot! Now, where was it? I know there was a piece of paper."

Sheafs of paper flew in all directions as she searched desperately for some mysterious missive on her dusty and over-loaded desk.

"Here it is!" she waved a letter triumphantly above her head as if it were the banner of a lost kingdom. She looked down at it.

"Oh, just in time! They want one of our journalists to go down and attend a one-week dressage course. Let me see the date."

Her weary eyes scanned the lines.

"Oh! it's not today, not tomorrow. but it starts the next day. I had forgotten all about this. Can you do it?" she asked anxiously.

"What – a one-week dressage course?" I asked tentatively. My heart was beating a loud tattoo inside my chest.

"A one-week dressage course at Porlock Vale Riding School. It's in Porlock, Exmoor – you know. It says here you should ideally take your own horse, but they can supply you with one if you want," she said.

"Yes, I can do that," I said.

I had heard of Porlock Vale Riding School, it was famed as the best riding school in the whole of the British Isles, and they had started up the first dressage lessons. I had read the book *The Horsemasters* by Don Stanford.

"You could write a piece about it. Perhaps half a page, even a full page if you got some good photos. You do have a camera?" she asked anxiously. I had Ann's camera. Hopefully, she'd lend it to me, or I could dash off and buy one right now.

"I can go, but I've got two horses, and the other one, not the dressage one, is in training for a one-day event, could I take both of them?" I asked, thinking this was crying for the moon.

"Look here's the letter. You ring them up and make arrangements. Thank goodness that's one more thing organised," said Miss Garter. She seemed to have forgotten about the article she had asked me to show her. In fact, we seemed to have leap-frogged right over any form of job interview. I feared that my piece on the Clattering Clutterbucks would be cast aside. I'd sweated blood over this small masterpiece. I thrust it at her, with the photographs and the negatives.

"You asked me to write something to show you," I said.

"Did I?" she asked helplessly,

I wondered how on earth they ever produced the wonderful magazine that I'd been poring over for years. She looked at my article.

"Well, it looks interesting. Take it and put it in the tray over there, it'll go to the subbies, and they can decide."

I was relieved that there was some order in the chaos. I even knew what a 'subbie' was, a sub-editor. It seemed I might get published. Luckily, I'd put my name and address and phone number on it. Hopefully, it wouldn't get lost forever. I daren't even wonder what I might get paid.

I decided that it didn't matter. It was all in the Lap of the Gods. I was off to Porlock Vale Riding School!

I decided that I would buy myself a camera before I went home. I knew that Ann was terribly fond of her own. If I broke it, I would be mortified, and it would cost an absolute bomb to replace. I caught the tube to Tottenham Court Road and walked up and down looking in the shop windows at cameras. There was such a huge variety. I didn't have a clue what I was looking for. I looked into each of the doorways until I saw a shop person who looked approachable and kind, an old man who might be the sort to work in a bookshop, with a bald head and glasses on the tip of his long twitchy nose. I would just have to take my chances.

"I want to buy a camera," I said, by way of introduction.

He began to give me a long lecture on types of cameras. I broke in with an explanation that might make it easier.

"I need something relatively simple that I can learn to use without a phone-book size manual, and with an adjustment, in case I want to do action shots. I don't need close-ups particularly," I said, congratulating myself on this summary of my needs.

"Hmmm," he looked at me over his glasses. "Well, young lady, I would suggest this. It is a very popular model and is relatively easy for the amateur to operate."

I watched him intently and made notes in my trusty notebook, that I now carried around like a badge of honour. I did some sketches as well so I could remember which nob or dial worked on what function.

"The lens cap," said the gnome-like man who was helping me, "is the most important thing, take it off to take a photo and put it on afterwards, and don't lose it, but here is a spare, just in case."

He thought I had the look of someone who lost things. Perhaps he was right. I was always losing one glove, or one sock as if they disappeared into black holes in the galaxy.

I rushed back to the station and took the first train to Rychester. I wanted to be sitting in my sitting room when I made the phone call to Porlock Vale. I didn't want to make the call from a public phone box. I leapt from the bus in Chatton market square and sprinted down to the cottage. Once inside, armed with the letter, I dialled the number. A very efficient-sounding woman told me that they had been surprised that the magazine had left it so long to finalise arrangements. I explained that I had two horses, one a dressage horse and the other a young gelding who was to compete in a horse trial in a month. Could I possibly bring them both down? She agreed readily and told me that I would be welcome to train around their cross-country course. I wrote down directions and told them to expect me about five o'clock the following afternoon. Then I hung up.

"I'm off to Porlock Vale! I'm off to Porlock Vale!" I sang out loud, dancing down the garden path to the field to call out to Balius and Skydiver.

"We've got to pack boys, a most wonderful time is ahead of us, and they're paying all our expenses!"

This was the most extraordinary thing! I had heard about Porlock Vale, but it had never occurred to me that I could go there for one of their famous training courses. I had to pack and prepare. All my tack, feed, grooming gear, the whole kit, and caboodle. All of my riding clothes and some dresses, in case there were social events. So much to do!

I was knee-deep in packing when Ann came home.

"You will never believe my news!" I shouted.

"You got the job!

"Yes, but that is the least of it!"

I went to the top of the stairs and grinned down at her, my mouth stretched wide like a cheeky Cheshire cat.

"They're sending me to Porlock Vale Riding School for a one-week dressage course, and I'm to write a piece on it!"

"Oh, Jill! That's the jam and double cream on top!" cried Ann, laughing up at me.

It was wonderful to have a friend who wished one well without a trace of envy. If this had happened to Ann, I'm not sure that I wouldn't have been pea-green.

"That's the riding school that the book, *The Horsemasters* was based on, isn't it?" shouted up Ann, as she started clattering around the kitchen. "I wonder if there'll be a glamorous bunch of students from all around the world, and you'll fall in love with some dishy Swiss prince who is destined for the Olympic games."

"I don't think they have a royal family in Switzerland," I said.

I staggered down the stairs with two suitcases.

"I've packed a lot of stuff, something for every occasion."

"Even for falling in love," she taunted me.

"Stop it!" I growled. "Anyway, I won't be a Horsemaster. I'll be one of those students that go there for a one-week course."

"Just what the doctor ordered," said Ann smiling at me, as she poured hot water into our battered old teapot. "Let's have a cup of tea to celebrate!"

We sat down to tea and toast. I told her all about Beatrice Garter, the cursory glance at my written piece about the Clutterbucks over which I had anguished for days, the rush to get there, and the stupendous thing that I could take both horses.

"Jill, it could only happen to you!" crowed Ann.

| 4 |

Chapter Four – Off To Porlock Vale

I headed across the country on the following day, got to Bristol, then turned south to the Exmoor coast. The only time I had previously ventured into Exmoor was when I had crossed it to get to Somerset on the dog-smuggling adventure described in *Jill Has Two Horses.* Porlock Vale was situated on the coast. Its back was to the moor and looking down to a picturesque bay. It promised to be a glorious week. My heart was singing, and I carolled along in my raucous voice.

This was the answer to my most secret and deep-seated fear that I would ruin my perfectly trained dressage horse. I would be learning from the best in England, except perhaps Henry Wynmalen. And there was a cross-country course around which I could jump Balius every day, in preparation for his eventing career. I felt as if I were at a point in this story when it should be the 'happy ever after' ending!

I arrived at the Riding School. I was part of the group called the Equitators, which was a bit odd. I did think that it sounded like a made-up word. This was distinct from the group of Horsemasters who did the three-month course to study for their BHS Preliminary Instructor's Certificate. Us Equitators were a privileged bunch. We rode in our lessons for two hours every morning and one and a half hours every afternoon. We did not have any stable duties. There was staff who attended to the horses, both working pupils and also the Horsemasters.

This left us with lots of free time to go into the village, down to the beach, playing tennis or just lounging around in the beautiful sunlit conservatory. There were bookcases filled with every type of horse book you can imagine, magazines – not only the popular *Horse and Hound* but also the very prestigious *L'Annee Hippique*, which was produced in Switzerland. It was a beautiful magazine with glossy pages, wonderful photographs and, reporting of all the international-level competitions. I decided that in the interest of furthering my journalistic career, I would read each of these magazines from cover to cover, in order to absorb the style and detail that would be part of my developing craft.

The Equitators were here for just one or two weeks for specialised courses. We stayed in the School's second house with separate stables to those of the Horsemasters' horses. Nor were we encouraged to mingle with the Horsemasters. I didn't mind. I was eager to meet my fellow students as I would be able to hobnob with the rather exclusive group of dressage riders in England. I imagined that just by the process of osmosis, I would absorb some of their knowledge. Sometimes even members of the British Olympic teams came here to receive instruction and help with schooling their own horses. I felt as if I had suddenly been elevated to another realm.

I had spent my first two hours helping to settle in Skydiver and Balius. They were in loose boxes beside each other. The bedding was thick, deep straw, the mangers freshly scrubbed, the buckets filled with fresh, clear water. Nothing was scrimped when it came to the care of the horses. Balius was staring at the other horses with the curiosity of a mountain sheep. But Skydiver took it in his stride. I guess he was used to being shipped all over the country to different places.

All the other riders had also bought their dressage mounts, and I was very eager to compare them with Skydiver but didn't want to go and rudely stare over their loose box doors. I would have to wait until our first lesson on the morrow when we were to all gather in the large indoor riding arena.

I was escorted up to the house by one of the working pupils, a very buxom, enthusiastic young woman called Ruth, who insisted on carrying my suitcases as if I were some sort of Lady Muck. She chattered away, telling me about the Riding School, the grounds, the gardens, and the tennis court. I listened intently. I wanted to ask her about her life as a working pupil but didn't get the chance. She knew that I was the journalist sent by *Horse and Hound*. She treated me as if I were a celebrity, which was a little embarrassing as I had never yet had an article published!

She put me in the hands of the Housekeeper, who was just like one of those women in the historical dramas on television. She wore a very housekeeperly type of outfit, all rustling and black. She was exceedingly polite, and as we progressed up to the first floor to my allocated bedroom, she threw out orders in a clipped and authoritative voice to various maids who were scurrying hither and thither.

I was put in a room to myself called 'Bluebell' with, you guessed it, wallpaper patterned with bluebells and matching flowery curtains. I had a view that looked straight down to the beach, and it was utterly divine. I wondered what it might be like to live in a house with a view of the sea, something rather special that I had never really considered before.

"Dinner will be served at eight o'clock, and we dress," she said to me imperiously after making sure I had everything I needed. After she left, I pondered on this remark. Had she thought I would go down naked? Then I realised that she meant 'dress up'. I looked around my room. There was even a small rose-patterned tin of home-made biscuits beside my bed should I feel peckish in the night. There was also a small table pushed up against the window with a chair, so I could sit and write letters, or in my case, type articles looking out to the sea, with plenty of inspiration flowing in through the open window with the tangy, briny smell.

I was thankful then that I had packed up my whole wardrobe of dressy clothes. If I had to appear in a different outfit every night, then I could probably just manage it. I felt as if I were standing on the threshold of truly becoming a grown-up. This feeling was intuitive because the very next day, I was to meet the most heart-stopping man who finally inspired me to jump feet first into the turbulent and exciting sea of romantic dreams!

At dinner, there were a dozen of us dressage riders, all women as dressage was still considered the province of females in stodgy old Britain. Another thing I noticed was the absence of anything approaching a common accent. They were nearly all double-barrelled, and some were titled. They were much older than me. There were introductions and I couldn't separate one name from another, let alone attach it to a woman; Mrs Southgate-de Long, Lady Telford-Talbot (alliterative double-barrelled!), Mrs Higgins-Latham, Lady Bentick-Throssel, Mrs Templeton-Watters, Mrs Dinwiddie-Marsh, Lady Rutherford-Flint. I felt like a little urchin from the village who had somehow inveigled her way onto this course under false pretences. I could only hope that my riding standard was not so far below them and Skydiver, a superior enough horse that I might put up a decent show.

Dinner conversation was lively and consisted of a discussion of what was apparently a famous controversy that had raged around the mid-1800s between the two rival schools in France. The *Baucher*, which had maintained that the hand must always act before the leg, and the *Comte d'Aure* who said that legs should always act before the hands. Then, there was a lot of quotation of *de la Guérinière*, who was a famous exponent before the French Revolution. I tried to follow the different lines of thought, but it was all Greek to me! I had never once considered such a thing having learned the aids in a very common-sense way at Mrs Darcy's riding school. The most I could remember along those lines was that the horse should be before my legs. I did begin to wonder if I was going to flounder out of my depth for the next week.

After dinner, I rushed upstairs and made notes on as much as I could remember about the argument. Perhaps it would all become clear as our lessons went along, or at least Linda might be able to cast some light before I had to write up my article. I could at least describe the house and grounds, the leisure pursuits and the training facilities. Such practical things were within my grasp, thank goodness! I suspected that the average *Horse and Hound* reader would be more interested in such pragmatic matters.

I hardly slept all night. I could hear the waves crashing on the shore below in the bay. I lay there listening for hours. I was excited about this new adventure and nervous about our first lesson tomorrow. I felt way out of my depth in this elitist group.

I woke early and dashed down to the stables to see Skydiver and Balius. They were both in good spirits, obviously enjoying their new environment and the very professional care that they were receiving. I got back for breakfast. Despite my nerves, I managed to eat a couple of good platefuls. The food was delicious, similar to the type of spreads that we had at Blainstock Castle when the paying guests were staying; fresh fruit, corn flakes, porridge, golden eggs, crispy bacon, French toast, ordinary toast, and best of all – kedgeree.

The other riders were down and without exception, elegantly attired in the most perfect made-to-measure riding clothes that could almost have been couture. I felt like a commoner amongst them, but I held my head high. I owned an excellent dressage horse, and I was here to learn. As an equestrian journalist, I considered myself a professional working woman, and I had no intention of tugging my forelock at overprivileged aristocrats, who thought they had blue blood.

This morning the talk centred around Diana Mason and her diminutive mare, Tramella.

"Yes, I've heard that Diana is certainly selected for Copenhagen," said Mrs Dinwiddie-Marsh, who I vaguely remembered was related to a sausage factory in the Midlands. I wasn't sure who Diana was, but all the others seemed to know her, or at least claim acquaintance. I felt hopelessly at sea. I was meant to be the dressage correspondent, and I didn't have a clue who was to ride at the European Championships in Copenhagen. This was going to be a steep learning curve.

"Yes, dear little Mell is some seventeen-years-old, you know," said Lady Bentick-Throssel.

"I remember Diana and Tramella riding for team gold in the European Eventing Championships. That was in 1954," said Lady Rutherford-Flint.

I tried to remember this and decided that an article on Diana Mason and her horse Tramella might go down a treat in *Horse and Hound.* My fingers were itching to make notes in my notebook. I felt as if I was going to have to gallop to catch up on the recent history of dressage in Britain.

After breakfast, we trooped down to the stable yard, and the staff helped us to mount, holding the opposite stirrups and handing us our riding sticks. Fortunately, I had remembered my gloves. Otherwise, I would have been the only one without. Walking the horses sedately down the lane, we rode through the entrance of the riding school and began to circle at the walk. It was ten minutes before our first lesson. I cast surreptitious glances at my fellow students' horses, and I was relieved to see that none of them seemed of better quality than my Skydiver.

At precisely nine o'clock in strutted a rather elderly, lean, elegant man who addressed us in very heavily accented English. He introduced himself as a Polish cavalry officer. He corrected our positions first. He was not intimidated by these high-bred English women and criticised them ruthlessly. Some of the riders were instructed to lengthen their stirrups, including me. I had to take them down two holes. It was very strange indeed to be riding with such long stirrups. I felt as if my legs were falling in straight lines down to the ground.

"It may feel odd, but it is correct," said Captain Romanski. "You will get used to it. Stretch your legs down and your head up to the sky and remember light hands and a flexible body. If you try and hold your body in the so-called correct position, you immediately begin to stiffen."

This shook me. All my riding life, I had tried to 'hold' a correct position. I had always arranged my students in a certain position and told them to keep it. It was now as if I had to learn the opposite of everything I had believed.

"The next thing is that many riders lean back, as it makes it easier for them to sit, especially during the sitting trot. But again, this is not correct. You sit straight in the saddle, the line of your back must not be leaning back. I do not wish to see any of you leaning back, and that includes you Mrs Higgins-Latham. You lean back far too much, as if you were in a reclining chair. It has become a terrible habit with you."

I wondered how Mrs Higgins-Latham felt about this criticism, but that is what we were here for, to learn, and to improve.

"Now, proceed to sitting trot, and let us see very straight backs, tops of the heads reaching for the sky, please."

With my legs hanging down straight, and my head reaching upward, I felt very weird, like a stretched-out piece of spaghetti.

"Miss Crewe, that is a very good horse you have, he makes it easy for you. Do not let him do all the work and carry you like a piece of luggage."

How very astute this man was! I realised then that he was right on the button. Skydiver did make it easy for me. I could have spent a week just practising what I had learned in the first half-hour. But the Captain pushed us on.

"The next thing is the horses' paces. This is the foundation of all work. Before we begin our advanced movements, our piaffe, and passage, and those fancy moves we work on the horses' paces. All the time, we aim for more lightness and more expression."

This was odd when you thought about it, how could a walk or a trot be expressive, but as he said it, I thought I could understand, but I don't think I could put it into words. And I'm not one often short of something to say!

By eleven o'clock, I felt as if I had been riding for ten hours; so much effort, and so many things to remember. We all dismounted, and I found that I nearly collapsed on the ground. The working pupils, who had been waiting on the sidelines, stepped forward and took our horses. We tottered back to the house for a sustaining cup of coffee or tea, and biscuits, and cakes.

The food revived me, and I decided that I needed to take Balius out jumping. Lunch was at one o'clock, and I would have to hop to it to be back in time for the next meal. I dashed off to the stables and tacked up before any of the ever-so-helpful staff came over to do it for me. Riding Balius was extra-curricular anyway, and I did like to do some things for myself. I could see the field where the cross-country jumps were dotted across the hillside, and off I went for a glorious training session on my own; twenty-five wonderful jumps set out in jumpable order. I was tempted to set off at a good 'hunting pace' and attempt a course, but I hadn't walked it, and decided that I would practice over two or three at a time every day and then when I'd done them all, we could go around as if it were a proper competition.

I rather enjoyed being out in the open air on my own. Maintaining my poise amid that bunch of superior women took quite a lot of energy. I made a mental note that I would never become like them. Although with my less than privileged childhood, I just didn't have that ingrained sense of entitlement with which they seemed to effortlessly mantle themselves. Self-importance was carelessly cast across their shoulders like ermine cloaks. My sense of poise, if I had such a thing, was shrugged on like an old cardigan.

The first jump I took was a very narrow stile that demanded concentration and careful placing, or one would be leaving a leg behind on one side. I circled Balius at a canter on the slope, concentrating on maintaining a consistent position whether we were going uphill or down dale. He was alert and eager. I couldn't help but notice that his stride was somewhat lumbering compared to the elegant finesse of Skydiver. Immediately, I felt guilty for having such a seditious thought. Balius was a perfectly decent mount, and I didn't want to get all superior over him!

I turned him towards the stile, and we jumped slightly uphill, which is always easier than downhill. He took off perfectly, and leapt cleanly, clearing it easily, but not over-jumping. He seemed to have grasped that on cross-country, one must conserve one's strength. He was such a clever and practical chap, I thought, deliberately praising him in my mind.

The next jump was a line of hay bales, and this was easy-peasy lemon-squeezy cool-bananas. I decided to take it at an angle so that we could practice something a little more technical. We set off at a slant, and Balius seemed to understand my intention. Again, we cleared it easily.

"What a wonderful, good boy, you are!" I said, patting him vigorously. I was determined never to let my love for him diminish.

The next was a drop fence, and I had a natural horror of drop fences. It was the one occasion when one had to lean back or else you would end up on the horse's neck. I chanted to myself, 'lean back, lean back' as we approached. Balius hopped down like a very clever cat. I was surprised. He seemed to have improved hugely since we had last jumped anything cross-country. When I had first trained him up in Scotland, we had done a lot of cross-country, and now he showed that he had retained the knowledge and matured at the same time. He was very good at this!

The next fence was straightforward, but big and solid, a fallen tree trunk. We cantered towards it at a fair pace, so we could have the impetus to clear it and gallop on. It was glorious with the wind in my face, and he leapt as high as Pegasus. I decided that this was enough for one day. I would jump them in reverse order back towards the stables. Then there would be time to walk him around to cool down before I dashed into lunch.

We circled wide and then galloped at the fallen tree and leapt over, up the drop fence, which was quite a stretch, galloped on to the hay-bales and then, steadied for the tricky stile. All clear! I slowed down, and we walked around some of the other jumps on a loose rein. I looked at them carefully. Tomorrow we would do more. My heart was full of love for Balius. He was my own, and I had trained him. That made him especially precious.

That night we had what I imagined was a sort of traditional evening's entertainment at house parties held in grand homes for posh people. There was a game of charades that was great fun, and I managed to guess two of the books and then had to stand up and perform.

Then the thunderbolt struck me! I had never thought it would happen!

One of the instructors, Jack Laskey had arrived late flying straight in from Europe, where he had been judging a dressage competition. He entered the room with a flourish. I saw a wave of fluttering and rustling spread around the gaggle of women. Every female face became glowing and pink as if illumined from inside by a rose-tinted bulb. He strode in, so handsome in his riding clothes, including extremely tight breeches. Afterwards, I did wonder why one would wear riding clothes while travelling?

I looked at him with interest, and then it flushed through me like a wave, a white-hot feeling that set me tingling. Here was a man worthy of a horsewoman's love. He stood in front of the crowd, so poised and at ease with himself, so sure that he would attract universal goodwill. Then, he recited a poem called 'Pegasus' by Eleanor Farjeon. The lines that struck me were:

The wing on his shoulder
Was brighter than fire.
His tail was a fountain
His nostrils were caves,
His mane and his forelock
Were musical waves,

There was a storm of applause from the audience. He bowed elegantly from his slim waist, his muscular shoulders dipping. He looked up, and there was a glint of amusement in his strange, penetrating dark eyes shot through with yellow lights. The women laughed like tinkling chimes and called 'encore', 'encore'. We all could have feasted our eyes and drunk in his words all night, but he demurred and slipped from the stage quietly and left the room. Undoubtedly, he didn't want to be besieged by the perfumed, jewelled but somewhat aged and adoring women. And I was one of them.

After he had gone, the room felt as if he were still there. Like all people of exceptional personality, he left a bit of himself behind, a warm, airy presence, a sense of something greater than the humdrum.

I dreamt that night that I was a poet, and in my dream, I was contriving poetical lines about a flying horse. I woke early and spent some time not only brushing my hair but discreetly applying a dusting of face powder and a light smear of lipstick. I went down to breakfast like an eager little fox terrier, expecting someone to be ready to throw me my ball. However, the elusive Jack Laskey did not appear. Perhaps the maid took him breakfast in bed so he could lounge for an extra half hour, like a prince.

I clattered down to the stables with the herd of excited women, clucking, and coo-ing and talking about 'dear Jack', and what a wonderful instructor he was. I felt in accord with the group this morning, but at the same time, there was the tension of rivalry between us. We would be flouncing around, flashing our charms against one another, in order to attract the male who had come into our midst. I secretly hoped that my relative youth would be an advantage. It was as if we were warming up in the collecting ring, eyeing each other up, and calculating our prospects against the competition.

The lesson that morning was taken by Captain Romanski. There was no sign of Jack Laskey. We would have to hope that he would be at morning tea. I turned my attention to dressage. I found that Skydiver responded very willingly as I improved my technique. As if he recognised true expertise and made an extra effort. But I became increasingly conscious that there was something missing in my relationship with Skydiver, nothing to do with the correct way of going. He seemed distant as if he were not prepared to engage with me emotionally. He kept himself to himself. I wondered again about his history and what had happened to him.

The Captain was relentless and worked us very hard. I felt as if my brain would burst. There was so much knowledge being crammed into it. I had learned a lot in Germany, but as there had always been the language difficulty, I had probably not grasped as much as I could have. Now I was bombarded with concepts and directives that made terrific sense and opened up a whole new field of knowledge about dressage.

At morning tea, there was an undignified scramble as Jack Laskey made an appearance. I hung back. I was too shy and unsure of myself. I had this strange sensation of going weak at the knees, like swallowing ice-cream too quickly. Lady Bentick-Throssel was the leader of the pack. She brayed the loudest and could elbow aside her social inferiors to get to Jack first. She monopolised him, but he smiled at her charmingly and played the gallant cavalier. I did rather admire Cynthia Bentick-Throssel, not only for her gorgeously imaginative name, which I understood was a combination of two surnames that had been joined together only two generations ago, but her self-confidence and bravado. She was not a good rider, but she had a rather magnificent giant horse that carried her hefty body valiantly. I had heard the other women sniggering and suggesting that he was part-Clydesdale. I imagined that Lady Cyn would have been more at home on the hunting field, but she had been steered into dressage by one of her grown-up daughters, and she did her best. I watched her standing far too close to Jack, her body was cylindrical rather than hourglass, and with her ruddy complexion, too much galloping in the wind over fences, she looked like a big red pillar-box.

I chose to believe that she couldn't possibly be thinking that Jack would be interested in her as a romantic conquest. I preferred to believe that she was trying to cultivate him for one of her five unmarried daughters, who had inherited her bold horsey looks. While the women concentrated on Jack, I maintained my focus on the divine morning tea cakes and biscuits, and then I dashed off to ride Balius around the cross-country course.

We started the session by jumping the four jumps we had practised yesterday and then went on to try the next. After the fallen tree was another drop fence. I jumped it several times. I knew that this was one of my weakest areas. There was a jump that I would later learn was called the Piano, which is terrifically imaginative. It was like two giant steps, two earth banks each a good three foot six inches tall. Then the next, which I would later learn was called the Coffin, but fortunately, at this moment, I was in blissful ignorance. It consisted of a treacherous gravelly slide with a deep yawning ditch at the bottom, with a solid post-and-rails set in the middle of the ditch. This was truly formidable, and I must admit I felt a little afraid. But I was determined to jump it. I could never progress in my riding if I did not push myself beyond my current limits. I promised myself I would only do it once, then the next was easy, a ditch and a bank up into the adjoining field. That would be my four new fences for the day.

I took three deep breaths and urged Balius down the slidey gravel slope. I resisted the impulse to shut my eyes and leave it to him. I kept myself firmly in the saddle, anchored with my lower leg around the girth. I hated the feeling of helplessness and then that horrible solid rail. If we hit it, we'd go headfirst. I tried to keep an even feel on his mouth and leaned slightly forward at the bottom of the slope with a strong encouraging push from my legs. He hopped neatly over. His Highland pony blood stood us in good stead. It was as if he 'had an extra leg' as the saying goes. I cantered on to the next upward jump, then swung around in a circle, missing out the horrible ditch then set off back over all the other jumps.

In the afternoon training session, Jack Laskey finally made an appearance, albeit a little reluctantly. He put us through our paces, and I saw him eyeing me critically. Much later, I realised that it was Sky-diver he was assessing. He was taking us through our paces with what are called the great classical 'airs' of the *haute école*. This was a giant leap from CaptainRomanski, who was insisting on correct foundational work on the paces. I heard one of the other women say, I think it was Mrs Templeton-Watters or possibly it was Mrs Dinwiddle-Marshy (or whatever her name was) say, 'finally we're getting some proper instruction for our level'.

He had us doing, or should I say attempting to do passage and piaffe, which are a type of suspended trot on the spot. These are quite spectacular movements, with very high steps and in slow motion, executed with cadence, balance and, controlled impulsion. Perhaps, I should say they were *meant* to incorporate all these elements. I smiled to myself to imagine what Captain Romanski would have said if he had witnessed the efforts of this group. I was to read later that before attempting these moves, riders should have obtained a state of perfect lightness. As competent as we might be in our group, I'm not sure that anyone had yet reached this stage. But what we lacked in skill, we certainly made up for in enthusiasm.

Passage was first attempted with just a slight forward movement, not more than a foot at a time, and piaffe is done on the spot. The transition from one to the other is crucial and requires a great deal of skill. Passage must be mastered before any transition to piaffe is attempted. Ideally, this learning process takes at least six weeks, alternating between a slow trot for fifteen to twenty strides, then a walk on a long rein, so that the horse eventually learns that speed is not wanted. Ultimately, he or she will begin to slow their trot down to almost walking pace. I had learned this through reading Henry Wynmalen's book on *Dressage; A study of the finer points of riding.* It requires patience and skill. It certainly wasn't the way we were doing it under dear Jack's direction.

He had us all trotting slowly, holding in the horses with a high hand position and pushing at the same time with legs in accord with the diagonals, like a kind of push-me-pull-me. Skydiver was the only horse who could do it, and I can absolutely assure you this was through no skill of mine! I was amazed when I felt him responding, and I almost let out a triumphant cheer. Jack congratulated me fulsomely, and I blushed bright red, knowing full well that this was solely due to Skydiver!

"Might I demonstrate on your horse Miss Crewe?" he asked.

My face was glowing like a beetroot. I dismounted so hurriedly that I landed with an inelegant thud on the ground. I was paralysed with love. I couldn't believe that he had chosen my horse for this honour. I tried to lengthen my stirrups for him, but I could only fumble around. My leathers were only just long enough for him, and I apologised for this profusely. Although, you're probably thinking that I was hardly at fault for not having second sight that a very tall man with long elegant 'boot' legs would be using my saddle.

He could certainly ride. In fact, he was a brilliant rider. His legs closed around Skydiver's sides, his hand held the reins lightly and masterfully, and he gave us a performance that I will remember all of my life. Later, upon reflection, I realised that he was a showman rather than an instructor. But that afternoon, we all watched spellbound, and I was bursting with pride that he had chosen my horse. He did a sort of performance that one might see at the Spanish Riding School. It lacked only musical accompaniment. He passaged at the trot and then transitioned to the piaffe. Then he pirouetted, a full turn on the haunches while Skydiver continued to canter on the spot. When he halted in front of us, we applauded. Skydiver then actually bowed, thrusting one foreleg forward and dipping his head. It must have been one of the theatrical tricks that he had been taught for the film business.

That evening I decided that if I were going to make any sort of impression that matched the performance of Skydiver, then I needed to wear my favourite evening dress. Mummy had given it to me as a Christmas present, a dark maroon soft velvet with tucks and darts all over, and a swinging flounce around my ankles. It gave me confidence, and I certainly needed that this evening, even just to hold my own on the sidelines.

Imagine how I felt when Jack spotted me making my way to a place down the side of the long table and insisted that I go to sit next to him. He then spent at least half of the dinner asking me questions about myself. I saw the other women shooting me baleful glances. He was fascinated with Skydiver, and I told him the whole story of Tatiana de Vere and the De Luxe Movie Horses. He told me that he would ask around and see if we could find out about Skydiver's life before that. I rather hoped he wasn't going to find out that Skydiver had been stolen from the Continent where he had been a famous dressage horse. That would put the kibosh on my plans, not to mention being in possession of stolen property.

After dinner, Jack said he was going out to the garden to smoke a cigar and asked me to accompany him. I was all of a dither. To tell the truth, I was scared. What on earth would one do in the garden with a man who has paid one particular attention. This wasn't just a lad of my own age, but a mature and extremely handsome man, admired by many women. He was also an absolutely amazing horse rider. I made excuses and fled upstairs. Then I spent at least an hour pacing my room, regretting my lack of courage, and wondering if another of the women had taken up the offer I had turned down. I was in such a state. I needed to talk to someone. I wished I could ring Ann, but that would have involved venturing back down to the phone in the passageway. There was no privacy, so even if I got her on the phone, I could hardly pour out my confused jumble of thoughts.

The next morning, I went down to breakfast and sat hunched over a large bowl of porridge with cream and golden syrup. Just as I was tucking in, feeling relaxed as Jack had not turned up for breakfast the previous day, he entered the room. A hush fell over the assembled company, and all chatter ceased. I may as well not have existed as he sat down next to Lady Cynthia and opposite Lady Rutherford-Flint. They were talking about a mutual acquaintance who had recently gone to live in The Netherlands, in order to train in a dressage stable over there. All my joy from his particular attention last night ran out of me like the last pint of water down the bath-pipe.

Jack seemed to know everyone and served up some very juicy tidbits of gossip that were meaningless to me as I didn't have a clue who these people were. I knew I should take note and try and remember. Gradually as I reported on the dressage fraternity, I would piece the jigsaw of names and horses together. But this morning, I was too embarrassed remembering how I had fled the evening before. Jack must think I was a ridiculous young girl who didn't know how to handle herself. And in that, he would be absolutely right!

I was glad to see that Captain Romanski was teaching again this morning. I heard one of the women telling him the work we had done the afternoon before. He didn't comment. But I imagined what he was thinking. We did, however, progress to leg yielding, shoulder-in, and travers. Skydiver was easily the best-trained horse, and I believe we acquitted ourselves creditably. The only criticism the Captain made of me was that I didn't put enough weight to the inside, the direction in which we were going, but rather let myself collapse with the weight on the outside. This was a very common fault, and nearly everyone else was doing the same thing.

Before lunch, I took Balius out. I felt rather strained, as if I had been trying too hard to improve on every front, so I contented myself with a steady canter around the cross-country course, just popping over the simplest and easiest jumps. I felt the need for some recreation. Everything was becoming far too intense. I wasn't sure whether I was looking forward to Jack taking this afternoon's lesson or not. To say I felt conflicted would be a gross understatement.

It was nothing like the previous afternoon. Jack came in and handed us out some dressage tests and suggested we learn them, and we would practise a few of the movements, but definitely not in order. On Friday afternoon, we would perform the tests and would be marked on them by himself and Captain Romanski. There was nothing complicated beyond shoulder-in and travers and some movements approaching collection and extension. This was a relief for me, if not for some of the other women who were straining at the bit to do the more advanced movements.

Jack ordered some of the working pupils who were standing by to set up markers so we could be sure to remember the different order of the letters. We began to do transitions from one to the other, and practice judging twenty-yard circles, always looking ahead to the next curve, not falling in or falling out too far, keeping our weight to the inside of the circle. I even forgot that it was Jack coaching us. I was so enthralled with practising these skills.

After dinner that night Jack suggested we all go off down to the village pub. With much squawking and chuntering, we dashed upstairs to change from our dinner dresses into casual outfits suitable for the pub.

There was much jollity and hooting as we trooped down the road into the village.

We went to The Star Inn, and the locals didn't give us much more than the odd appraising glance. They were obviously used to people from the riding school descending on them. The landlord was friendly and served us drinks with great gusto, and free dishes of salted nuts to nibble on, and make us thirstier. The atmosphere was riotous when a darts match was set up between the villagers and us. The village won hands down, and drinks were bought for all. I enjoyed it because I was just part of a noisy crowd. No-one took much notice of me. I observed Jack surreptitiously. He didn't seem to favour anyone in particular. He was friendly, jovial, entertaining, and adored by all. Most of all me!

On Thursday, Captain Romanski continued training us for the dressage tests, instilling the importance of correct and accurate transitions. Jack took over along the same lines. We practised square halts and saluting the judges. We each got to sit up in the position where the judges sat and watched each other. In this way, we could understand just how much they could see, and what they were looking for. There were no more fancy moves, nor over-ambitious high-school movements.

By Friday, I was still nervous that I hadn't learned the test correctly. The other women seemed to know the test well, having all been competing regularly. I decided to forgo my last cross-country practice on Balius. Instead, I took him to one of the outdoor arenas and rode through the test from start to finish. Our shoulder-ins were rather clumsy. Our attempt at travers, which is like the opposite of a shoulder-in, was barely discernible. But I did remember the test. I was so pleased with Balius and made a promise to myself that as soon as we were back in Chatton, we would be practising our dressage like mad.

After lunch, we retired to our rooms to dress up in our best riding outfits. This dressage test was to be the 'real deal', a good practice for when we were competing in the future. I had decided to plait Skydiver's mane and tail. His mane was so silky, thin, and even, that it was easy to plait. Not like Balius, whose mane was rather thick and scruffy.

The dressage test was run as if it were a real competition. We were called by working pupils acting as stewards, and then we trotted in one by one to bow to the judges. Skydiver was so professional I felt as if we were floating through the movements. We were awarded the highest marks, and I knew this was down to my horse, and not to my riding. I was determined not to get a swelled head.

The last evening was something of a celebration. The other women made a huge effort to charm Jack and competed against each other to be the wittiest and most entertaining. I sat back contentedly, in the background. Strangely, I imagined that Jack was watching me. I dare not hope what that might mean. After dinner, I found him at my elbow, and he steered me out of the room and into the conservatory. I was absolutely terrified, but at the same time, thrilled. Was he going to declare his undying love for me?

I admonished myself with the mantra 'compose yourself', 'compose yourself'. I took some deep breaths.

"I've a wonderful idea," said Jack, in a low, conspiratorial voice.

Perhaps he wanted us to run away to Gretna Green? I forgot that we were both of age and could get married in the local registry office. But what would Mummy think?

"There's a dressage competition in Tavistock on Sunday, and I can swing some late entries. The two of us could go with your horses. I could ride Skydiver in one of the advanced tests, and you could take your Balius in a novice test."

For some reason, my mind stuck on the fact that he had remembered Balius's name. I was sure that this meant something. Then I grasped the suggestion. We would go away, the two of us. Without being surrounded by the other women. We could talk, really talk, get to know each other. I could discover the real Jack Laskey beyond the theatrical, social self.

"Oh, yes!" I breathed, and clutched my hands together, giving a good impression of a maiden who has been given a sight of heaven.

"Entries are closed, but I know the Secretary and can ring her up and get us late entries. Do you have competition names for the horses, or are they just Skydiver and Balius?"

This was an intriguing question. It had never occurred to me that they might compete under different names. I did seem to have wandered into the world of double-barrelled surnames. Perhaps I should add Micheldever to my own surname, Jill Crewe-Micheldever, or Jill Micheldever-Crewe. It just didn't sound right.

"No, no, just Skydiver and Balius will be fine," I replied.

"We can go in your horse box, leave tomorrow morning and stay overnight for the competition on Sunday," replied Jack, in a wonderfully take-charge way. "Don't say anything to the others. You know how people can be. Envy of you and your beautiful horse."

It was a secret! Almost an assignation! My heart fluttered. A horsey assignation was much more my style than a stroll in the garden after dinner!

I lay awake that night and imagined myself as Mrs Jack Laskey. We would live in a house down near the harbour, looking straight at the bay from halfway up the hill. We would have a field at the back of the house, but our horses would be stabled at Porlock Vale. I would not only gain my Preliminary Instructor's Certificate, but go on to acquire the Instructor's Certificate, and we would both teach at Porlock Vale, but also be free to travel over to the Continent and compete in international dressage competitions. The other women would dance around Jack coquettishly, but he would have eyes only for me. It was a golden dream, and I went to sleep drifting on a cotton wool cloud looking down at my future life from a great height in a mood of utter bliss.

The next morning at breakfast, there was a general stir and bustle as everyone prepared to leave. Jack and I were to go after lunch, and I decided that I would take Skydiver around the cross-country course for some fresh air and exercise under the blue sky. He had spent yet another five days of his life in an indoor arena. He should enjoy a jaunt in the great outdoors.

Jack caught up with me in the stables and suggested that he might ride Balius. We set off, just the two of us. I saw that Jack was not one to relax and enjoy the quiet countryside. Immediately, he began to canter in circles around us and put Balius at the hardest of the cross-country jumps, slithering down the gravelly slope and over the solid post-and-rail fence set in the ditch at the bottom. I admired Jack's fearless riding style. Skydiver walked along with perfect equanimity. He showed no inclination to follow Balius and throw himself over any jumps. He really was a strange character, not like any other horse that I had ever owned.

"He's a jolly little pony, this one!" shouted Jack at me, after they had galloped at the huge solid tree trunk and cleared it magnificently. "You should do well eventing."

Then I noticed that Balius was puffing. If it had been anyone else but Jack, I would have been annoyed that he had pushed him too hard. He had to get fit for the one-day event, now just a few weeks away, I reasoned to myself. I was in such a state of mind that anything Jack did could be justified.

"What are your ambitions?" I asked curiously, wanting to plumb the depths of my hero's soul.

"Well, dressage is the new thing, and everybody else in England just wants to jump around the fields. I suppose three-day eventing would be ideal as I am rather good at jumping cross-country. But it is such a lot of work to train the horse for all three disciplines," he said.

Immediately my brain leapt to the conclusion that I would be the trainer in the background, and Jack would take the horses and compete. What would it be like to be the wife of the World Champion, gold medals at the Olympics?

We rode on beyond the cross-country course to the moorland and walked down the road that ran beside it. It wouldn't do to take Skydiver over the rough ground. He was too valuable and had to be wrapped in cotton wool. Especially for the competition tomorrow. We returned to the stables. It was quiet, now the gaggle of women had left with their cut-glass accents and loud self-confidence.

| 5 |

Chapter Five – Going Away with Jack

We left for Tavistock, and it was Jack who drove, him being such a masterful man. I was terribly excited about the dressage competition! But then I remembered that looking forward to something would surely put a blight upon it. I tempered my runaway feelings.

I spent Saturday night on a camp bed in the back of the horse box, tossing and turning restlessly, trying to remember my dressage test. Jack had booked himself into a hotel. On Sunday morning, I was utterly ajitter with nerves. I began to plait Skydiver's thin mane. My fingers felt like bunches of bananas. I wished Ann were here to do it for me. Jack didn't turn up until the sun was high in the sky. It was just as well that I had prepared both horses.

I mounted, and Jack pushed my leg back to check that the girth was tight enough. Being in such close proximity to him, made me very nervous. He smiled up at me.

"Don't forget to smile at the judge when you bow. You have such a lovely smile!"

I went bright red! An outright compliment!

The moment passed. The stewards were calling for Jack. There was no time for him to warm up. He vaulted into the saddle and cantered elegantly across the smooth green turf.

I rode Balius over so I could watch his test. They swept through the entrance. I was spellbound. They literally danced through the test. The thought that swirled around my brain – this is *my* horse! It is hard to describe, but they definitely had that 'expressiveness'. I was sure they would win by miles.

At least watching Jack and Skydiver had taken my mind off my forthcoming first test on Balius. I began to warm up. There were about six competitors to go before I was called. I conscientiously trotted and cantered and eventually trotted down the centre line to bow to the judges, I remembered every move as if it were stamped on my memory in indelible ink. Balius had improved enormously since we had gone to Porlock Vale. All the teaching that I had received had undoubtedly improved my riding. I left the arena on a loose rein, exuberant and looking around to find out how Jack had judged my performance. But he was nowhere in sight. Several people called 'well done' to me as I rode back to the horse box. Skydiver, still saddled, was tied up. Not even his girth had been loosened. Jack had disappeared. Something must have happened, and he had had to rush off.

I unsaddled both horses and threw light rugs over them to stop the annoying flies buzzing around. I made sure they had filled hay nets and buckets of water. Still no sign of Jack. I decided to walk over and buy myself a lemonade and watch some of the other competitors. I was feeling a little disconsolate. Where had Jack disappeared to? I hoped he hadn't fallen over, hit his head and got concussion forgetting who he was and what he was doing here. I thought of going over to the Secretary's tent to ask if there had been any accidents. There had to be a reason for his absence. I was sure that he could never be so unchivalrous as to desert the horses and me.

I was walking past the benches beside the arena, where the spectators watched, when I heard a loud cackling of laughter. I looked over and spotted Jack amid a lively throng of very smart-looking people. I waved vaguely towards him, but he seemed to turn away. I didn't dare to go over. I walked on alone and sat by myself at the end of a bench. Waves of shame swept over me. I must have done something wrong. I was too embarrassing for Jack to acknowledge me. I wasn't grand, or sophisticated enough. I felt very conspicuous sitting there all by myself, without a friend in the world. I tried to concentrate on the remaining competitors in the large novice class. Some of them were competent, and some were drearily hopeless. I tried to imagine what I might say to each if I were their instructor, to help them improve. These constructive thoughts were a weak attempt to try and mitigate the yawning awfulness inside me. What had happened between Jack and me? Had I in some way deeply offended him? Or perhaps he had an excellent reason to be amongst that group of people, and he didn't want me to interfere.

I felt hot tears pricking my eyeballs, and I dashed them away, like a child lost in the shopping centre. Then I saw him, loping over towards me, his long elegantly booted legs taking great strides as he approached. He smiled with the sweetest grin, his brown eyes shining.

"Jill, here you are! I've been looking for you everywhere! Do come over and meet some people. The results won't be announced for at least another hour."

I exhaled deeply. My angst drained away. It had all been an awful misunderstanding. My fears at being deserted and unwanted were ridiculous. I pulled myself together. I had to stop these childish fits of emotion.

"Everyone is terrifically impressed with your most amazing horse. They're predicting a glorious future for him!"

My heart warmed to that group of people who had seemed like unfriendly strangers just half an hour ago. He took me by the hand and towed me over to join them. Ten people were sitting on folding chairs around the open boot of a Rolls Royce. There were the remains of a splendid spread.

"Here, champagne for the owner of the celebrated Skydiver," cried a middle-aged man, thrusting a glass towards me.

I wasn't really in the habit of quaffing champagne in the middle of the day, especially with the prospect of a long drive back, but I took the glass and smiled my thanks shyly.

Jack then introduced me around, and there was, as usual, a lot of double-barrelled names. I seemed to have fallen into a world of those with two names. Exalted company! I wondered if I would ever feel at home with such people. Of course, I had known the Cholly-Sawcutts for years. They were double-barrelled, but the girls had always been such blots that it had been more amusing than socially exclusive. Perhaps in time, I wouldn't even notice. I must take heart. Anyway, Jack only had one surname. I loved the sound of his name, Laskey, somehow so exotic and fascinating.

"What do you do dear?" asked one woman, dressed as a spectator, not a rider.

"I write," I said shyly.

"Really! What do you write?" I sensed genuine interest.

"I've written pony books for years, and now I've just begun to write articles for *Horse and Hound*," I replied.

"Really, how interesting," she said. "Perhaps you would like to visit us and do a piece on my daughter. She'd love to be in *Horse and Hound*."

"Is she a dressage rider?" I asked.

"Yes, she was competing today, in the same class as Jack and your magnificent horse. I rather think it will be between him and her for winning honours. Sylvia, darling come and meet Jill, what did you say your name was?"

"Jill Crewe," I replied, thinking that this might be an interesting prospect for an article.

Sylvia Latchington-Field tramped over and smiled. She was not the most photogenic girl, with a large, square horsey face and protruding teeth.

"How do you do?" she boomed at me.

"How do you do?" I replied.

"I rather like your horse, that Skydiver, I haven't seen him around the traps before," she said.

"No, he was working as a horse in films, you know ridden by actors. I first discovered him when they filmed Macbeth up at my people's place, Blainstock Castle," I replied.

You might notice how subtly I supplied my credentials, as someone whose family owned a castle.

"Jack told us that you were attending a course at Porlock Vale. I've had a lot of lessons from Captain Romanski. He is rather good," she said.

"Yes, he is brilliant, so much to learn. I've only really started to focus on dressage before it was just showing classes and low-level showjumping," I replied. "But I have entered my grey in the Houghton Heath one-day event in a couple of weeks. It will be his first horse trials."

"Oh, that is exciting. Of course, I've hunted all my life, and now there's this dressage lark, but perhaps horse trials might suit me better," she said. "You say there's an event at Houghton Heath."

"Yes, it's just a tinpot affair," I replied. "Nothing like Burghley or Badminton."

"Well, that might be just the thing, combine this dressage with jumping, much more interesting!"

We fell into a lively discussion of our horses and their good points and bad points, and I found that despite her double-barrelled name, she really was a good egg.

"You must come and stay with us some time. We could school together," she said. "It would be fun to work with someone. You know that it was Jack who found this horse for me. We shipped him over from The Netherlands."

Jack the Horse Coper, I thought. He was a man who was out and about and knew a lot of people. I realised then that I really didn't know anything about his background. Somehow this made him all the more attractive and intriguing. Perhaps he was a member of some European royal family who had had to go into exile, like Prince Philip.

They were calling over the loudspeaker that the results were about to be announced and would we gather unmounted in front of the Secretary's caravan. Jack touched my elbow and taking my arm; we walked together. I stumbled over a clod of grass, but his attention had strayed for a moment, and he was talking to another woman. I only just saved myself from sprawling on the ground.

They began with the lower-level classes, and I found that Balius and I had come a respectable sixth in the novice class. There was no rosette, but our name was called out, and I was more than satisfied with this result. Later, I would scrutinise our marking sheet and hopefully learn invaluable lessons for the future.

Jack smiled at me and clapped me on the shoulder. They droned on and on and finally came to the highest-level class, and starting from sixth they called out the names of the prize winners.

"Second is the Honourable Sylvia Latchington-Field riding her own Glenmarton."

We all clapped like mad, and I looked over to Jack as we realised he had won the class. Skydiver had won! This was a tremendous achievement!

"First is Jack Laskey riding Miss Crewe's Skydiver."

Jack strode out the front and smiled graciously and thanked everyone concerned. He had won a rather large trophy, and as the owner of the winning horse, I would have the trophy to take home. For a moment, I was sad that I hadn't won it myself, but the credit must go to Skydiver himself, and I was utterly thrilled.

Jack returned to my side, and impulsively I went to kiss him on the cheek, merely congratulations but unfortunately, he was too tall, and my peck fell short and landed on his neck, which was a bit weird. He drew back and smiled at me, and I felt reassured.

We walked back to the horse box, reading our results sheets.

"Well Jill, this is where we say good-bye, I'm to stay the night with friends, so I'll see you off. Thank you so much for letting me ride your wonderful horse."

I was a little dazed. I had thought that we would drive back together to Porlock Vale tonight; that I would be invited to stay another night, and somehow arrangements would be made that Jack and Skydiver compete again. I hadn't thought how that was possible but had hoped that the masterful Jack would suggest a plan.

"Oh," I said helplessly and stood looking at him in dismay.

"I'll help you pack up the last of the gear," he said. "Are you going back to Oxford tonight, or heading up to Scotland?"

This, at least, was gratifying. He had been sufficiently interested in my life to know that some of the time I lived in Oxfordshire, and some of the time in Scotland. He *had* been listening!

"I'll go back to Oxford tonight. I have the Houghton Heath one-day event in a couple of weeks," I said. I was desperately hoping he would ask for details and tell me he would come to watch. Perhaps he was planning to turn up as a surprise. He waved me off as soon as the horses were loaded, and I set off back to Oxford. I had a lot to think about!

I arrived back at Pool Cottage before midnight. I felt utterly wasted, like a chewed-up piece of string. Ann hadn't been expecting me. The cottage was in darkness, and Black Comedy was in one of the loose boxes.

I settled Skydiver in the other and put Balius out in the field. I looked up into the night sky as if beseeching the heavens. A new moon, thin as wire, gave a strangely fierce light over the smoking chimney of Pool Cottage.

"I wish ... I wish ...," but I couldn't put it into words. I had wished for a dream dressage horse, and that wish had been granted. But somehow? Wearily, I left everything in the horse box and went upstairs and tumbled into my bed and slept until late the next day. What an emotional merry-go-round. My thoughts were scattered to the four winds.

| 6 |

Chapter Six – Houghton Heath

The one-day event at Houghton Heath was only two weeks away. The dressage test was dead simple, and the jumps wouldn't be more than three feet high, but I was determined to be prepared, like a boy scout! Every morning I schooled, first Skydiver, and then Balius on the Common doing our dressage movements. I also tried Skydiver with a few extra advanced things. I loved the passage and piaffe that Jack had made us do at Porlock Vale. It felt wonderful with that suspended slow-motion action. I was always hoping that Susan Pyke might ride by and observe our advanced riding, but there was no sign of her. I had heard on the grapevine that she was back from honeymoon, but I imagined she was too busy being a grown-up wife in Rychester to be riding around Chatton.

In the afternoon I would take Balius back out, and we did alternately long, slow work to build stamina, trotting slowly along grass verges for miles. I would practise lateral movements when there was a rock, or a ditch and we would leg-yield to either side. On the fast work days, we would go to the hills and gallop up lickety-spit and then walk down and then gallop up again. Balius's muscles were bulging now. I felt rather proud of how he was coming on. I found myself planning our training, our future events. I even began to write up schedules on the backs of envelopes. I tried to banish the unwelcome thought that all this planning was rather like my cousin, Cecilia, who always had her activities planned days in advance. I had thought myself rather happy-go-lucky, letting things happen, but that just didn't work when it came to competing in the higher echelons of equestrian endeavour.

Ann and Henry had said they would come along and help me at Houghton Heath. And we set off - a jolly band of musketeers. Certainly, having a professional vet in tow was a boon! Clever Ann for finding a vet! I felt the urge to talk about Jack all the time, but I made a strenuous effort to limit my remarks to only one every ten minutes. I even entertained the very secret thought that he might turn up.

"Did you do much jumping at Porlock Vale?" asked Ann.

"It was just a dressage course, but I did jump Balius around their cross-country in the break between the morning and afternoon sessions."

"One of my farmers said that his daughter did the course to become an instructor last year," said Henry.

"Really!" I exclaimed. "So, what happened, is she working now?"

"Well no, apparently she had her eye on the young farmer next door, and she was playing hard to get. So, she shot off on this course for three months, and sure enough, absence made the heart grow fonder," said Henry, laughing at this tale of human caprice.

"Men can be such simple creatures," said Ann wisely, as if she were well-acquainted with the way that the minds of men worked.

We all sang along to the radio to a song that we loved, 'We're all going on a summer holiday . .'

"Why don't you do that course, Jill?" suggested Ann.

"Me!"

"Why not, get yourself a certifibubble, then you'll be on an even playing field with Serena," replied Ann, knowing how my dark thoughts had occasionally slithered towards the Saintly Serena.

"But I'm meant to be becoming a journalist," I said, almost plaintively.

"You could write about the Horsemasters' course. They might even give you a discount."

My mind was leaping about all over the place. It would mean three months of being near Jack. We really could get to know each other properly. Otherwise, we might never see each other again, unless I really could get to top-flight dressage competitions, which he was also attending.

"I should think you'd have a great time, the other students will be younger, much more fun than all those stuck-up double-barrelled ladies and duchesses," said Ann.

"But I couldn't take my own horses," I said, thinking of all the objections. "I finally get myself this wonderful dressage horse, and I have to put him on ice for three months."

"You can leave them with Linda. They'll come to no harm. In fact, Linda training them will be all to the good."

I had to admit that she was right there. Linda was a better rider than me.

"Once you've got a certificate you might be able to get a proper job you know, on the Continent, speak German and have a go at some real dressage competitions."

Now that was an idea. Again, my dream of competing on the international stage hovered like a miasma in my imagination.

"They did have fun, the Horsemasters, they were always dashing around. They had to wait on us Equitators, but it was like we were the privileged visitors, they were the ones that really belonged."

"You might even get a job instructing at Porlock Vale itself," said Ann with a sly grin at me and an elbow in my ribs. She had probably guessed that I was stuck on Jack.

My mind was racing. What a plan! I would have to ring and make sure they had places left in the September course and find the fees, but my last royalty cheque should cover a lot of it and perhaps Mummy and Richard could give me my birthday and Christmas present towards it. Getting educated had to be seen as a worthy activity.

My thoughts were buzzing along these lines until we arrived at the venue. As if in confirmation of this wild idea, the first person I saw was

Sylvia Latchington-Field. She called out a cheery welcome in her loud voice that sounded like a trumpet.

"Jill Crewe! I was hoping I'd see you here. See I've come to try my hand at horse trials!"

Her rather enormous square face was beaming, and she marched towards us, teeth to the fore.

I saw Ann looking askance.

"She's a jolly girl," I said. "Come and meet her. Definitely a decent sort."

I made introductions all round, and we unloaded the horses.

"So which horse are you riding?" I asked Sylvia.

"Oh, not the dressage superstar from Holland, you know the one that Jack found for me. I've brought my old hunter, who is rather my best friend. Dear old Nobby, we've been hunting for three seasons now. I've given him a bit of a crash course in dressage, and he's responded manfully, or should I say horsefully." She guffawed at her own joke.

Just the sound of the name 'Jack' uttered on the lips of another sent a thrill through me.

"Have you seen anything of Jack since the dressage at Tavistock?" I asked as artlessly as I could manage. Dear Sylvia didn't shoot me a sharp look. I don't think her mind ran along such lines.

"Ummm," she responded with a frown. Obviously, Jack didn't feature in her thoughts a great deal! "I think Mummy mentioned that he was staying with Lady Blatch-Kiddington. You know he is an itinerant house guest."

I latched on to this piece of information, with a few dark thoughts directed at Lady Blatch-Kiddington. She sounded like a woman from the 1920s. Immediately, I wondered if I might not invite him up to the shooting at Blainstock in August. That was a 'house party extraordinaire'. Now that *would* impress him!

"Jill!" called Ann. "You've got to get ready. Your dressage test is in less than an hour!"

"Gosh, yes," cried Sylvia, "I'm on too! See you in the collecting ring!" She strode off.

I began to dash around, feeling shame-faced at having been distracted, once again, by the thought of Jack.

"You haven't got your number!" said Ann accusingly. "Jill, what on earth is wrong with you?"

"I just got muddled," I muttered, my face flushed dark-crimson.

"I'll get your numbers for you," said Henry, leaping to the rescue like a gallant knight. "You get on and start riding in."

I scrambled into my riding coat, donned my hat and mounted. Ann had plaited Skydiver perfectly.

"You're riding third on Skydiver, and then at the end of the list on Balius," said Henry, loping back with my numbers.

I bent down and tightened the girth and trotted over to the area where the steward was calling in the competitors. The first horse and rider combination were already halted at X, and bowing to the judges sitting in the car.

I noticed people staring as we zoomed across the showground. Skydiver was a cut above the other horses, and I felt like we were making an exhibition of ourselves. I tried to ignore the hard stares directed at us. I shut out the comments that floated across the air. I had entered under the pretence of doing the jumping as well, and had planned to retire after the dressage. I felt uncomfortable as if I were doing something deceitful.

Skydiver didn't seem to pick up on my confusion. He stepped out with his long rhythmic stride in his usual professional manner. We began to circle, and the steward called out my number and name. I nodded acknowledgement at him. I was so flustered that I did nothing but trot in circles. I had planned on a complicated set of exercises before we went in, but that had all gone by the wayside.

I did cast a few glances at the horse and rider doing the test before us. They were utterly abysmal. They had halted incorrectly with a trailing hind leg, then cut all the corners, and their circles looked egg-shaped. I wasn't sure whether this was reassuring or not. I felt like Skydiver was standing out like a sore thumb. I had to stop comparing myself with others and focus on doing the very best we were capable of.

The steward called me over. I was able to cast aside my torturous self-consciousness as we trotted through the entrance at A. I made sure we were dead straight to halt at X, saluted and smiled at the judge. We then proceeded at a trot and turned left at the top, making sure to ride into the corner and half-way down the long side I went into a smooth twenty-yard circle. I didn't lose my way, and we managed to transition accurately. Our circles were smooth and circular, and we struck out on the correct leg during the canters. I left the arena discreetly patting Skydiver's elegant neck. We rode back to the horse box.

Ann had saddled Balius now and was leading him around. The timing was quite tight. I couldn't imagine riding two horses without at least one helper. I slid off Skydiver's back and mounted Balius. He would need more time to work and settle down. I couldn't just rely on his expertise to carry us through. We had done enough competing here and there for it not to be completely strange for him, but he was still relatively inexperienced and curious, and he would be distracted. Then I realised I would have to go over and withdraw Skydiver from the showjumping, which was due to start before the dressage was finished.

I told the Secretary that I was withdrawing Skydiver from the competition.

"Why?" she asked suspiciously, giving me a hard stare.

"He's not quite right. I don't think I should jump him."

"He looked pretty good in the dressage arena," she barked at me.

I felt a chasm opening up before my feet. It had started as a tiny white lie, and now it was growing in front of me. I was tempted to embellish it with more falsehoods, but then it would turn into a story of monstrous proportions, and I was sure to be caught out. My name would be mud in the world of horse trials!

"I just don't feel confident, I'm sorry, but we must withdraw," I muttered, conscious that my face was bright red. I felt sure she knew that I was lying. I rode off. Again, I had to focus on riding in Balius and stop thinking about other people. This time I had sufficient time and presence of mind to try the shoulder-in technique to increase impulsion and straightness. Balius was going rather well. I felt hope shoot through me. He was becoming more rhythmic and balanced in his strides. We struck into a canter, and he led off on the correct leg. I felt confident that we would do our best.

It took some time before the steward called us in. I saw that the showjumping had begun. It was a simple course, just eight fences between two feet six and three feet. The first horse jumped clear, and the second went clear also. If I had not withdrawn Skydiver, I would have been next. Most of these horses were better at jumping than dressage. Then the steward called us over, and we entered the arena. I remembered to smile at the judge, just as Jack had instructed me at Tavistock, and we were off. I was pleased with Balius. I felt as if my recent training and doing the test earlier on Skydiver was paying dividends. I was getting the hang of this.

We left the arena, and I trotted back to the horse box so I could change from the dressage to the jumping saddle. I had had no chance to walk the showjumping course, but it was fairly straightforward and watching others jump I could see that the distances between the jumps were standard, nothing tricky or difficult.

There were another ten horses to jump before us. Sylvia was doing her round. She was riding a very hunterish-type of horse, plain brown with rather thick legs, a short back and a large head with the hint of a Roman nose. She went clear. I realised that I had underestimated her ability. She was a jolly good rider. She certainly knew what she was doing, with a workmanlike seat and accurate placing of her horse in front of every jump.

I walked Balius around on a loose rein until there were just two horses to go before us. Then I gathered him together, and we jumped the practice jump a couple of times. He felt dependable and reliable beneath me. Not everyone had gone clear. There had been several refusals at a substantial oxer that faced away from the collecting ring. A couple of horses had also knocked the gate on the far side of the arena. It didn't look very solid. It seemed to swing a little in the breeze.

We were called in, and I took my time cantering around before we went through the start. I sat lightly in the saddle and tried to breathe confidence into Balius. He gave a little toss of his head as if to say, 'don't worry about me – we've got this under control'. The bell went, and we cantered through the start. We headed straight on to an inviting brush fence, over and then on towards a double, with two simple strides between them, then left towards the gate on the far side of the arena. I could clearly see it swinging in the breeze, and this made me nervous. I shortened Balius up too much, we took off too early, and he just rapped it with his hind hoof, and I heard it fall behind us. That meant no clear round. I forced myself to concentrate, so I didn't make another stupid mistake.

I rode back to the horse box. Ann took Balius from me and insisted that I sit on an upturned bucket and eat a cheese sandwich. She gave me a bottle of orange pop. Henry came hurrying over.

"Some of the dressage results are up. Skydiver is twenty penalty points ahead of the whole field."

I grimaced a little at that. I'm not sure why I felt such a fraud, but I did.

"And Balius?" I asked.

"He's sitting eighth at the moment, that's with Skydiver, so without him, he's seventh. There's not much in it though. How did you go in the showjumping?"

"Five penalties, we knocked the swinging gate," I replied, suddenly shot through with hope, perhaps we might be placed.

"I imagine it'll be decided with the cross-country. I understand that's the way of things with horse trials. Would you like me to walk the course with you?" he asked.

"That's kind," I said. "You and Ann. I think the horses should be alright by themselves here. That woman in the trailer there would probably keep an eye on them."

The three of us set out with a map in hand, and I had a pencil so I could make notes.

"It's just under two miles," I said, reading through the information.

"Short and sweet," commented Henry.

"Not such a hike," said Ann.

"Twenty jumps," I continued.

Like the showjumping it was pretty straightforward, nothing tricky and certainly no death traps. The whole event had been designed for novices. It was perfect for Balius.

"Hey, Jill! Hey, Ann!" came a shout from behind us when we were halfway around.

We saw Clarissa Dandleby stomping up the hill behind us.

"I thought it was you Jill, in the dressage on some fancy-schmanzy dressage horse. Surely you're not jumping that thing around this course?"

I groaned. Clarissa had always been extremely unattractive in body, as well as spirit, and, now, she managed to whack me right in the place where it hurt.

"I've retired him. I'm riding my other horse," I replied evenly.

Clarissa was now upon us, her boiled gooseberry eyes squinting against the sun, greasy hair pulled back in its usual unattractive bun.

"I didn't think you were into horse trials, I thought it was point-to-pointing and nothing else," commented Ann.

"There's nothing on so I thought I'd give it a bash. This fancy tarra-diddle of dressage is a joke, but it means I get to ride around the cross-country course. But there's not much in it, is there?" she replied in a brutish voice.

"Have you heard anything of Susan since she got back from her honeymoon?" I asked curiously.

"Love's young dream!" snorted Clarissa derisively. "I suppose you two will be marching down the aisle soon." She fixed her gaze calculatingly upon Ann and Henry.

Ann laughed lightly, taking this outrageous comment in her stride. Henry managed to maintain his composure.

"We're still in the wooing stage," Ann laughed. "And you Clarissa, how are you going in the matrimonial stakes?"

"I'm getting hitched next month," said Clarissa in a matter of fact way.

This stopped us in our tracks. We stood there with our mouths open in astonishment.

"Who on earth is going to marry you?" I asked in a terribly tactless way.

She grinned at us and didn't seem to take offence.

"One of my father's friends has popped the question, and it's a good offer. He's got a stable over near Cambridge, jump racing that's the thing. I'll have my pick of horses. It's a good deal."

"What a delightfully pragmatic approach," said Ann facetiously. But her tone was lost on Clarissa.

"Not bad. Suits me to a tee. Don't worry I'll be sending you invites to the bash. Old Charlie is insisting on a big do."

"Have you chosen your wedding dress yet?" asked Ann. My mind was having trouble conjuring up an image of Clarissa in something white and frothy.

"Mother is sorting that out. I've no time for fittings and all that palaver," she snorted. "Anyway, got to press on. I've three horses to jump around this course."

We stood there and let her march ahead of us. We could hardly wait for her to be out of earshot when we fell to discussing this most extraordinary event.

"I'm going to be the only old maid amongst us," I groaned, but secretly I was imagining myself floating down the aisle and Jack waiting at the altar, with his most debonair and charming smile.

"Can you imagine the events of the first night of the honeymoon?" said Ann.

We laughed at this. It was all at Clarissa's expense. Henry remonstrated.

"Come on you cackling hyenas, let's get back to the cross-country, you don't want Clarissa to beat you at your own game Jill."

We went back to looking at the map of the course and strode on to the next jump. I made notes along the way. I wanted to get this totally right. By the time we got back to the showground, there wasn't much time before I was due to ride. They were about to send out the first horse and rider, and it seemed that quite a few had dropped out, which made me feel a bit better about Skydiver retiring.

Ann helped me saddle up, and then I was trotting large circles around the exercise area. I began to realise how fit a horse had to be for this type of event. I was thankful that I'd put in the hours working Balius over the last few weeks.

The steward called us. We were in the box, and then they were counting us down.

'Ten seconds to go," shouted the steward.

Now we were galloping at a cracking hunting pace, and the heady joy of speed possessed us as we flew over the first hedge, down a slope over a small, reassuringly solid wall. Balius felt perfectly balanced beneath me. We had to jump into a copse, and for a moment we were blinded as we headed into the relative darkness, but Balius quickly readjusted his gaze, and I steadied him for the stile back out into the sunlight. His ears were pricked, and we felt perfectly attuned to each other. This is the meaning of life I thought to myself.

There was a slightly tricky in-and-out made up of sheep pens. Again, I steadied him. Then, there was an uphill gallop with a solid three feet post-and-rails at the top. I let Balius choose his own pace up the hill, and he didn't slow down. He was hardly blowing so I felt sure that he had enough left in the tank to make it to the finish. He popped the post-and-rails as if it were nothing and then there was a ditch with a rail in front of it and a sharp turn to another hedge. I had decided when I was walking the course that I would take the ditch at an angle, so we were set up to fly the hedge, followed by the gallop home over a fallen log, another post-and-rails and then splashing through a water jump that wasn't much more than a large puddle. We galloped past the finish flags. I was brimming over with exultation. Somehow dressage was never going to be this exciting!

I walked Balius around a bit by ourselves at the bottom of the field after we were through the finish. I wanted a few moments alone with him to enjoy the last waves of exultation. It was possible to have twin passions I decided, look at Diana Mason who had won team gold in an eventing competition in the early 1950s and had then gone on to win gold medals in dressage on the same horse. Nothing was going to spoil this feeling of having just jumped a glorious round! I felt as if the world lay at my feet. I rode back to Ann and Henry, who were waiting to congratulate me.

"Oh Jill, you did go clear, you must have, you were so fast, no time faults I don't imagine," said Ann.

"Jolly well done, old girl," said Henry.

We turned to watch Clarissa galloping in through the finish on a lean, rangy looking bay thoroughbred. She threw the reins at a middle-aged looking man, almost old, and jumped on another very rangy looking thoroughbred.

"I'm not sure how she actually knows which is which," said Ann. We stared at the man, thinking he must be the fiancé.

"He looks pretty old," I whispered. I mean Jack was older than me, but he was gorgeous and dashing. This man just looked ancient and worn out.

"There's no accounting where the fairy of love will fall," said Ann.

"The fairy of love is closely related to having a racing stable, in this case," I said.

We went back to the horse box. After rubbing down Balius, we put all the tack away and packed up ready to go.

"I love this end-of-the-day feeling," said Ann. "Another blissful horse competition."

"Don't you miss the riding?" I asked.

"Not really, I just enjoy the whole thing, getting ready, plaiting up. I guess I was destined to be a groom."

"Or a pony club mother," said Henry smiling at her proudly.

I gulped at this, but Ann didn't seem to mind. She smiled back at him. There did seem to be a very good understanding between them. Perhaps they had already discussed how many children they wanted.

"You can be a pony club big sister with Hamish," said Ann. "Do they have a good pony club up there in Scotland?"

"Not very close to where we live," I replied.

"Well, that can be a project for you," she said.

"I think I'll leave that to Richard. He knows a lot about horses, and I can see him as the District Commissioner," I replied lightly. I was rather hoping that I didn't turn into the maiden aunt who lives on at the castle while everyone else enjoyed conjugal bliss.

We could hear them calling everyone to the Secretary's tent for the results to be announced and we rushed over. I was thrilled when Balius and I came third. It was a very decent result, and I was filled with pride for my horse. There was no way I was going to let my affections for him be eclipsed by my new ownership of Skydiver.

I clasped my yellow rosette and took the dressage sheets. I would be examining them in detail later. Now it was time to head for home, back to Pool Cottage, tea and cheese on toast and that wonderful time of talking over everything that had happened today.

On the way back we sang a little to the songs we liked on the radio.

"You're going to be competing at Chatton Show, aren't you?" said Ann.

"Yes, that's the plan. I want to take Balius in the open jumping. That's been my ambition," I said. "And I thought I'd take Skydiver in a hack class and a riding class."

"Oh, that's fun, I'll plait him up for you," said Ann.

"I've been roped in to help with the stewarding," said Henry, "and I'm to be the on-course vet as well."

I realised then it was only a few more weeks to the show and then I had to head straight up to Scotland to help with the guests who came for the shooting.

"What's happening with *Horse and Hound*?" asked Ann.

"I sent off the article about Porlock Vale last week. I haven't heard back yet. I'll probably see it published before they contact me," I replied.

"Did they publish the Clutterbucks one?" asked Ann.

"I don't know, I've had no word from them."

"You should ring them up," said Henry. "Don't just let it slide. That's the thing about being a freelance you have to keep pushing if you want to get anywhere."

Of course, what he said made total sense, but my mind was on ringing Porlock Vale about booking in to be a Horsemaster in September.

| 7 |

Chapter Seven – Top Hat and Tails

I was hopping around like a cat on hot tiles on Monday morning, waiting for Ann to lead Black Comedy down the road to the field by her parents' house. I felt a little embarrassed about my plan to get back to Porlock Vale. I was sure Ann would guess my ulterior motive, pursuing Jack Laskey like a besotted fan. As soon as she was out of sight down the drive, I dialled the Porlock Vale number. My fingers were shaking.

I recognised the voice of the housekeeper. There was one space left on the September course. I gave her my name, and she told me the cost. I promised to send a cheque that day. They would post me information. You may be wondering why I didn't want to shout my plans to the world. It was a huge decision, a big chunk of my life, quarter of a year and at a time when I could have been training Skydiver, but I felt rather desperate to get back to Porlock Vale. I was so sure that Jack was The One. I was determined to place myself firmly in his orbit.

The next phone call was to Beatrice Garter at *Horse and Hound.* She was irritatingly vague and at first couldn't remember who I was, which was rather galling.

"I came to see you a few weeks ago. I gave you an article about the Clutterbucks who keep their horses in London. You sent me to Porlock Vale to a dressage course. I posted that article off to you the other week," I said, my voice high-pitched with irritation.

"Oh, of course, you're Jill Crewe!" she exclaimed. As if I didn't know that!

"The articles I wrote," I said. "Did they use them?"

"I don't know dear, don't you read the magazine?" she replied blandly.

"Normally yes, but I'm away at the moment," I said getting increasingly irritated, thinking I would have to go around to Val and Jackie Heath's and look at the last few weeks' issues. Their father had had a subscription for years.

"Presuming, they have published at least one, how do I get paid?" I asked.

"You'll have to talk to Accounts, that's not me," she said.

I restrained myself from screaming in annoyance. I gritted my teeth, to pitch the idea for my next article.

"I thought I might do a piece on Diana Mason, one of the leading lady dressage riders in Britain. What is particularly fascinating about her and her little mare Tramella was that they had started out in three-day eventing and even won a gold medal. Then after a rather bad accident, they went on to specialise in dressage."

"I know all about Diana," said Beatrice. "Yes, that sounds good. You do that". And she hung up as if I were annoying her with meaningless details.

I paced up and down. Obviously, working as a freelance journalist required not only getting good ideas, finding material and skilled writing but also sufficient tenacity to deal with magazines to get your work published, not to mention getting paid. I decided to go around and visit the Heaths to look at their magazines. I wouldn't ring, I would just ride by on Skydiver and hope that someone was home.

I had gone to school with the Heath twins. Their real names were Valeria and Jacqueline Horrington-Hobday-Heath. Then, it struck me. So much for feeling uncomfortable in the land of people with two names. My old school friends had three surnames! They had always been rather good riders. Even when I had first started learning to ride on Black Boy, Val had been winning riding classes in under-fourteen events. When we were all still at school, they had both won prizes at Richmond Horse Show. Their father was a well-known local equitation expert. For years the twins did everything together, but Val had grown rather big-headed and sidey, whereas Jackie was more down to earth. They did tend to be over-mounted. They rode blood horses that pranced around impressively but didn't have the best of manners.

As I rode over there, I imagined that they would greet me with the news that they were both getting married, like Susan Pyke, Clarissa Dandleby and probably Ann in the near future. All my friends are getting married! I arrived in their stable yard and found Jackie there by herself, pushing a broom around rather aimlessly.

"Yups!" I called.

"Oh, Jill! How are you. I'm dying of boredom by myself. Nothing much going on," she said.

"Where's Val?" I asked curiously.

"Haven't you heard, she's gone off to America!"

"Wow! America! What's she doing there?"

"She is staying with friends in Virginia, in the middle of horse country. They love her British accent and think that she's a world equitation expert."

"That sounds fun," I said, "good work if you can get it. Why didn't you go with her?"

"I wasn't invited," replied Jackie sourly.

"It must be weird, having done everything together for so long, then to be separated," I mused.

"Yes, I feel like just half a person without her. Apparently, she's going great guns though. Doesn't sound like she's missing me at all."

"Oh, poor you! But you must just buck up. You can go out and do your own thing now."

I wasn't exactly sure what her own thing was.

"I'm at rather a loose end. The whole riding and competing thing has palled, I'm afraid."

I looked at her in astonishment. I couldn't imagine ever thinking that riding and horses were boring. It struck me then. I had always envied the Heath's their horsey father who managed their riding careers, but now I saw that it might be something of a disadvantage if one decided that one didn't want to do it anymore. Ann had turned away from the competitive life and just hacked around the lanes on Black Comedy, and her mother probably hadn't even noticed. My mother was always interested, but she certainly wasn't pushy. Poor Jackie!

"Are you studying? Working?"

"No, nothing. I seemed to have come to a complete full stop."

I didn't dare ask what her father thought of that. Jackie hadn't even noticed Skydiver, my new dream dressage horse. Normally, she would have been onto it first thing.

"I was wondering if I could browse through the last few weeks' of *Horse and Hound*?" I asked.

"Sure, why not. Do you want to push him into a loose box?"

"Thanks," I said, sliding down to the ground and undoing the girth.

"Why do you want to read *Horse and Hound*?" asked Jackie, but more with politeness than real interest.

"I wrote a couple of articles for them, and I want to see if at least one of them has got published," I said. "You know that April Cholly-Sawcutt is writing for them, about showjumping."

"No, I didn't," said Jackie.

She was so sad. I wondered if she might be heading for a nervous breakdown. But I was a little uncertain how one acted with people who might be suffering nervous breakdowns.

"Had you heard that Ann is back at school so she can get into Veterinary College?" I asked.

"Yes, I think I heard that," said Jackie vaguely.

It seemed that nothing was going to rouse her.

I began with the *Horse and Hound* the week following my presentation of the Clutterbuck article. I turned each page carefully, scanning from top to bottom and down every column.

"Oh, look! There's Diana Mason!" I said, pointing to a picture of a big dressage event near London.

"Yes, Dad knows her. He was talking to her last week."

I looked up like a pointer sniffing a rabbit, or whatever it is that pointers hunt for.

"Do you think he would introduce me to her, so I could ask her for an interview?"

"I don't see why not," replied Jackie listlessly.

I kept turning page after page, magazine after magazine. Then I saw it. The photo of the ponies emerging from the front door. I read it quickly. They had included everything I had written! I was jubilant!

"Look! Look! This is what I wrote!" I said, thrusting it in front of Jackie. She roused herself sufficiently to at least glance at the page I was brandishing.

"That's good."

"Oh, wow! Oh, wow! Do you think I could keep this copy? Or would that be a frightful imposition?"

"I don't suppose Dad will mind. He reads them every week but never seems to go back and refer to them."

Mr Heath strode in at that moment.

"Whose horse is that in the box?" he asked in a loud, matter-of-fact manner.

"It's my new horse, Skydiver. I got him to do dressage."

"Dressage!" he exclaimed and snorted like an old carthorse. "New-fangled rubbish! Ruins a good horse!"

I looked at him in astonishment. I would have thought he was more up to speed with the current developments on the equestrian scene.

"Jackie told me that you knew Diana Mason," I said, thinking that surely anyone acquainted with the woman who was almost the Queen of Dressage in Britain would have a more current view.

"Yes, she's certainly got this dressage bug," he said. "She was a decent rider in the past, part of the British eventing team."

"Would you mind giving me her contact details? I want to ask her if she will do an interview. I've been doing a bit of writing for them. Look! This is my first article."

He looked at it.

"Yes, I read that, jolly good stuff. Have you heard that my Val is in America at the moment, she's wowing them over there!" I realised then that he was a bit of a skite.

"Yes, Jackie told me," I said, feeling uncomfortable. There was no denying his paternal pride, and I felt sorry for Jackie, who must feel like the family failure.

"I better get going. Jackie will you come over for dinner one night soon. Ann is turning into rather a good cook these days, and we can have a girls' night in."

This sounded a bit weird as Ann and I virtually had a girls' night in every night, it's not like we were out gallivanting all the time.

"Let's make it tomorrow night," I said.

"Sure," she replied, but without enthusiasm. "About seven?"

"Yes, that'll be good. See you then."

I waved good-bye and rode away. I was thoughtful. Val in America was just what one would expect. She had always been brimming over with self-confidence to the point of being irritating, but I had never seen Jackie this low before. I would talk to Ann. She was sure to be able to come up with something we could do to cheer her up. Ann was good like that.

I was taking both horses up to do some schooling at Neshbury Common most days, trying my very hardest to build a better relationship with Skydiver. He still felt a bit like a push-button horse that performed for anyone who rode him. I wasn't used to this type of horse. Both my ponies had been individuals, and we had enjoyed deep friendships with a mutual knowledge of our personality quirks. That had been especially so with Rapide, who was what one might call an 'original'.

The next day Skydiver and I were practising the passage and piaffe up on the Common when I noticed a very old man in a baggy hacking jacket leaning on a shooting stick, watching us intently. Perhaps he was looking for contenders for the next Olympics. My imagination ran totally out of control. I couldn't resist showing off, and we performed some one-tempi changes which we managed to pull off, due to Skydiver's skill rather than mine. Then to finish off my impromptu showing off we did half-passes at the canter, which is basically cantering on a diagonal.

"Bravo!" shouted the old man, his voice thin and reedy drifting over to us.

We walked over to him.

"Never seen anything like that up on the Common before," he said, smiling benevolently. "Would you consider giving a display of this dressage at the Show in a few weeks?"

Of course, I knew that he was referring to Chatton Show.

"Do you think that would be the sort of thing that would go down well?" I asked doubtfully. "I'm not sure that Chatton is ready for dressage."

"Grassroots!" he said as if that explained everything. I think he meant that if we promote a sport at the lowest level, it will help it to develop and spread throughout the nation.

"Do you really think we're good enough?" I asked.

"Have you got the top hat and tails?" he replied, not bothering to answer my question.

"No, not really, just ordinary kit," I replied.

"Well, my wife was a great enthusiast and had the proper outfit. She passed away last year, but you look about the same size, why don't you come over and see if it fits. I'm on the Committee you know, and I think this would go down a treat."

"I'm Jill Crewe," I said, thinking that I'd never seen this man in my life and I'd been going to nearly every Chatton Show for many years.

"I'm Colonel Ted Mottley, new in the village, moved up from Dorset, but keen to get involved," he replied. "Are you a local girl?"

"Yes, I've lived here forever, in Pool Cottage. Now I go up to Scotland a lot as my mother lives there."

"Just what we need, someone local to promote the art," he said, smiling. "Do come over this afternoon, I'm in the white house at the end of Cherry Tree Lane."

"I know you've only just bought it, haven't you?" I said.

"That's right. Come for tea, and you can try on the kit. It's not new, but it was the best quality, you'll look a treat on that lovely horse."

So, it was a date, and I set off later that afternoon. It was only a ten-minute walk, and I didn't want to drive the horse box. It would look a bit strange to be going to tea in a big truck.

I had never been to this house before. It was at the top of a slope, long and low and painted a pale cream, rather than white. There was a large front garden, which had been arranged into three wide terraces. I began to climb the shallow, broad steps to the front door. The first terrace was like a miniature formal garden, a maze of small box hedges. The second terrace was dominated by a very large lily-pond that sat beside an odd little summer house that rather had the look of a folly built in the style of the Taj Mahal. The third terrace was a wide expanse of perfectly manicured, as if clipped with scissors, emerald-green lawn with a riot of bright summer flowers growing along its edges. This arrangement looked new, and I thought perhaps that Colonel Mottley must have worked on it to take his mind off the loss of his dear departed wife.

I knocked on the iron-studded oak door and heard footsteps coming down the passageway.

"Ah, Miss Crewe I have been waiting for you. I've found dear Elsie's clothes. There's actually quite a few pairs of jodhpurs and a blue jacket and a couple of tweed jackets as well as the fancy outfit. She always had the best, looked after her clothes. Come into the sitting room."

My eyes were drawn immediately to the sofa where there was indeed a rather splendid array of riding clothes. I walked a little closer and looked at them carefully. The top hat and long-tailed coat were the best quality. I crossed my fingers that I was the right size.

"What do you think?" asked Colonel Mottley, a little anxiously as if he were trying to make a sale rather than kindly giving them away.

"They look brilliant," I said earnestly. "Would I be able to try them on, to make sure that they fit?"

"Yes, yes, I'll leave you to it. I'll go into the kitchen and prepare tea. When you've finished just come out into the passageway and call me. Don't worry. I won't disturb you."

I felt a tiny bit uncomfortable. He seemed like a very nice man, but now it occurred to me that I was going to be undressing in a stranger's house and no-one even knew where I was. I reasoned it out to myself. If a stranger really did intend to harm one, then they could just as easily attack you with your clothes on than off. I banished such nervous thoughts firmly. I mean how many violent attackers lure their victims in with the promise of second-hand riding clothes?

I tried the tailcoat first. It fitted well, perhaps just a little loose around the shoulders and tummy but it would give me plenty of room for growing, in case I was going to put on weight. Not that at nineteen I was exactly approaching middle age! There was a large mirror hanging over the fireplace, so I was able to look at myself, twisting this way and that. Then I placed the top hat on my head. It fitted well, neither perching precariously, nor sliding down over my eyes. It was exactly one inch above my ears. But still, it appeared rather odd, and I wasn't sure that my face was made for such a hat but once mounted it would certainly look the part.

"Oh, yes! Thank you, God! Thank you, Elsie and Colonel Mottley," I said quietly to myself.

I whipped off the coat and quickly shrugged on each of the other coats in turn. Again, they were slightly large, but not even enough to make it worthwhile getting them taken in. Then the jodhpurs; three pairs of cavalry twill, light beige, medium beige and cream and again they were a little large around the waist. I didn't know whether I should show the Colonel how they fitted or whether it might remind him of his dear Elsie and upset him. I decided to get back into my own clothes then went out to call him.

He emerged from the kitchen with a silver tray loaded with sandwiches and a whole iced cake and a big teapot.

"Oh, what a splendid tea!" I exclaimed. "The clothes fit almost perfectly, just a trifle loose but that will give me some room to grow into them."

"I'm so pleased," he said, smiling widely. "Now you have no excuse not to give a wonderful exhibition at Chatton Show. It will be rather a coup, on my part, to have found such a good rider locally."

"I've ridden at Chatton quite a few times," I said. "Though not on Skydiver. I've only just bought him. I'm also taking my other horse, the one that I trained myself. Chatton Show, is quite a big deal you know, over the years we've had some very famous show jumpers turn up."

I could have gone on to tell him that when I was thirteen, I remembered watching the open jumping and had marvelled at the magnificent horses and their skilful riders soaring into the air over white-painted jumps. I was certainly no newcomer to Chatton Show!

"Well then it's guaranteed that you'll turn up," he said, again smiling. "We have some new blood on the committee. There is me fresh from Dorset and also a quite formidable young woman who you probably know as she has been competing at Chatton Show all her life, Susan King."

"Susan . . King," I stumbled over her new married name. I should have known that there would be a catch in this deal. "Yes, we've known each other for many years. We went to school together."

"Splendid!" he exclaimed, obviously imagining that we were bosom buddies.

"Brilliant," I said faintly. Thinking that Susan would be sure to object to the idea of me giving a specialist riding display. She still treated me as if I were twelve years old.

I feasted on the sandwiches. Then the Colonel, who was obviously a sensible man cut me a rather large slice of coffee and walnut cake, and I consoled myself with the thought that I had just acquired a whole new collection of riding clothes. If the rest of the committee decided they didn't want me to do a dressage display, then there was always the riding class and the hack class for Skydiver. Colonel Mottley gathered up the clothes and carefully placed them in a worn but elegant suitcase.

"You may as well have the suitcase," he said sadly. "There'll be no more trips for Elsie and me."

I felt his sorrow. Here was I at the beginning of what was shaping up to be a rather magnificent life, and he was slipping away alone at the end of all his happiness.

"Do you have any children?" I asked, thinking that would be some consolation.

"Yes, we had a daughter, but she's gone off to live in New Zealand. She's been after me to go and visit her so I guess once I'm settled here in the new house, I should make the journey," he said.

"And grandchildren?" I asked, hoping that there would be future generations for im to look forward to.

"No, she's a career woman, she's not married and no children. It's so disappointing."

I said good-bye and walked off down the driveway carrying the suit-case of treasure trove. It was better than any jumble sale I had ever been to!

That night Jackie turned up for dinner. Ann had concocted an inter-esting meal of chicken and apricot pie, which she said she had dreamt about. She was practising her cooking skills, perhaps preparing for her future life as a vet during the day and wife and mother of a tribe of pony clubbers the rest of the time. Jackie and I picked our way through the pie with supreme tact.

"I'm thinking that I might write a recipe book," said Ann. "You'll be my guinea pig, Jill!"

I stretched my mouth into a smile in a semblance of joy at this thought!

I changed the subject swiftly to the exhibition I was to give on Sky-diver and immediately Ann gushed forth with suggestions.

"Are you going to dress up?" she asked.

"Well yes, I've got this absolutely splendid top hat and tails, and other stuff as well, which Colonel Mottley gave me. It used to belong to his dead wife."

"Dead woman's clothes," said Jackie in sepulchral tones.

"No, I mean, what is your horse going to wear?" asked Ann.

"Nothing," I barked back.

"I know! Tassels and stuff, like the Arabs," said Jackie with a wicked grin. It was a shame that when she finally started to buck up, it was to taunt me.

"You're not taking this seriously, are you?" I challenged them.

"Let's dash over to Mummy's and get some records then we can try out bits of music," suggested Ann.

Mrs Derry was astonished to come upon us bagging the records.

"What on earth are you girls doing?" she asked.

"We're choosing some music for Jill to ride to at Chatton Show," said Ann, as if this were the most natural thing in the world.

"Are you dancing?" asked Mrs Derry incredulously.

"Yes," I laughed. "I suppose I am, or rather Skydiver is dancing and I'm going along for the ride. We have to find something that has a good beat in time with the rhythm of his canter."

"You need a metronome for that," snapped Mrs Derry, shaking her head and backing out of the room.

Ann had a little record player that Henry had given her. We spent the evening playing bits and pieces and prancing around the tiny living room at Pool Cottage. It didn't take long before we were rolling around the floor in fits of laughter. Finally, we found one that I rather liked the sound of, one of Haydn's symphonies called 'The Clock'.

"Do you think the band will be able to play this?" I asked.

We always had a brass band at the show.

"You can ask, if not they can play the record over the loudspeaker."

"I'll go around and talk to Colonel Mottley and see what he can arrange."

"Next we need to design your whole exhibition, like choreography," said Ann.

In the end, we were exhausted.

"This is not as easy as it looks," said Ann, throwing herself into an armchair. "I'm so tired I'm practically decomposing!"

"I have to go home," said Jackie. "But it's been a wonderful evening. I'd love to come over and perhaps we can try out different ways of doing it with Skydiver."

"I would appreciate all the help I can get," I said, thinking at least we'd cheered up Jackie.

This went on for days, and I found it hard to keep up my showjumping training on Balius. Jackie turned up a lot, and we even went out on a few rides. I let her ride Skydiver, thinking that such an amazing horse might inspire her to start riding properly again.

Just one day before Chatton Show, I trotted Skydiver up to Neshbury Common for one last practice. To my dismay, I saw that the chain of perfect summer days was breaking up. Dark grey clouds were gathering on the western horizon. A summer storm brooding, the air still and unnaturally hot. Perhaps a deluge of rain would fall on the following day, and Chatton Show would be drowned.

I ignored the weather and practised our shoulder-ins. I felt much more at home on Skydiver now. He was still 'the perfect horse'. I hoped that the day he misbehaved I would be ready for it! I still knew nothing about his background. I did not want to contact the scary Tatiana and ask her. Perhaps one day we'd run into someone who recognised him and could tell me something about his history. Please God that he wasn't stolen!

The storm clouds gathered above us as I concentrated on our training. I had mentally marked out an arena. I had decided that I would ride through our planned exhibition, just once a dress rehearsal. We did it perfectly, and I was congratulating Skydiver as we walked on a loose rein around the edge of the Common. Deep in thought, I didn't notice how the storm was rushing in on us. There was a torrent of air rustling around the treetops, and I looked up to see the familiar surroundings had suddenly taken on a sinister air. Heavy clouds had massed in an ominous red-tinged bank on the edge of the sky, glowering above us. I would have to make for home.

Then I discovered that Skydiver did have a psyche. He had feelings and fears the same as the rest of us, but he must have been doing a massively good job in suppressing them and behaving impeccably. Unfortunately, this type of repression perhaps increases the boiling emotions within. I was about to discover that he was a real horse, after all!

The first clap of thunder rang above our heads. A double fork of lightning snaked down to the ground not far from us. Skydiver began to tremble, and I felt him panicking. I turned him for home, and we set off at a brisk trot. He felt very flighty beneath me. The next clap of thunder set him well and truly completely off his rocker. He threw his head in the air and was galloping madly. His legs flinging about wildly in an unco-ordinated pace. I wasn't totally unprepared, and I stayed firmly in the saddle, but my mind was streaming with pictures of utter disaster. My horse running head first into a truck, a bleeding carcass on the road!

This was bolting in its pure form, not just being 'run away with'. I had perhaps experienced something like this once before when the Cortman kids' horse Blue Shadow had run away with me at a show. I had certainly read about it in horse books. This was, indeed, a full-scale bolt. That is when the horse is completely set in itself to gallop full-tilt to death or a standstill, whichever comes first. A thundering blind gallop is terrifying to watch, but a thousand times worse when one is on the horse's back. The horse lacks any predictable motive, like a madness, the eyes wide, the movement jolting, swerving, ungoverned.

I tried to turn him before we hit the road and I just managed to run him round in a wide curve on the Common – at least we were avoiding traffic. I then discovered the problem of having a well-trained dressage horse that can turn itself inside out with gymnastic flexibility. I never would have believed it before. He ricocheted from one bush to the next, and leapt sideways, then I felt him coiled like a beast ready to spring, he was snorting, and there was foam flying from his mouth. He was utterly terrified, and I was infected with his fear.

Then, there was another clap of thunder, and I felt him crazed beneath me. I wondered whether I shouldn't throw myself to the ground and just let him go – but that was not the act of a responsible horsewoman. I shortened one rein, and he was running with his head bent around to my knee like a sort of action figure with a rubberneck. Time seemed to be stretching before us, and I had a vision of my dream horse charging like a frenzied dragon with a goblin on his back into an eternity of thunderclaps and forked lightning.

Then came a miracle. Another horse and rider came cantering up beside us. It was one of Mrs Darcy's old cob geldings, and onboard was the perfect Serena of the long legs and owner of a 'certificate'.

"Whoa! Whoa!" she said in a commanding, deep, calm voice. They came right up beside us and taking one rein she crowded the cob in so he was pressing against us. Miraculously, Skydiver seemed to calm with the presence of another horse, especially such a well-built, plain and steady horse who had probably never experienced a frenzied moment in his life.

The cob was called Chunk by the way, and he was chunky that was for sure. Gradually he slowed down, and Skydiver stuck to him like a limpet, and we were trotting.

"Tell me which way is home, and I'll come with you," said Serena.

I was so relieved to have been rescued that it was only as we slowed to a trot that my Ignoble Self kicked in. If it could have been anyone but Serena to have rescued me! It was almost unbearable, but not quite. I was shaking now, in the aftermath of such a tremendous shock.

"Down this road, but I think we should be alright now," I replied.

"It's no trouble, dear old Chunky, he's very obliging," she replied, smiling in such a sweet and kindly way that I felt like a jealous old woman.

"Wendy told me that you have a certificate as a riding instructor," I said as we rode. My words hung in the air. It was as if the terrifying experience had jolted my darkest, secret thoughts out of me.

"Yes, my father insisted that if I wanted to work with horses, then I had to get some sort of qualification. Now I've got the BHS Preliminary Instructor's Certificate."

"What was the course like?" I asked.

"It was very hard work. I could already ride, and I'd been instructing the beginners at my local riding school for years, but the pressure was relentless. I did get to ride a lot of different horses, quite difficult horses, perhaps that was the thing that I learned the most from, or maybe the cross-country jumping, which wasn't something I'd done a lot of," she replied thoughtfully.

"Do you think it makes you a better instructor?" I asked.

"It's certainly given me a lot more confidence, and I think that, in turn, instils more confidence in my students. They know that I know what I'm talking about."

"I'm booked in at Porlock Vale to do the course in September," I told her. She was the first person I had mentioned this to. Strange how we feel closest to those who stir up the most negative feelings in ourselves. I wondered if I might suddenly pour out to her my secret hopes of Jack Laskey. My mouth seemed to have taken on a life of its own.

"Porlock Vale has a wonderful reputation, you will have a terrific time," she replied. "He certainly is a beautiful horse. Wendy was telling me he's very advanced in his dressage training. You are fortunate," she said, without guile or envy.

"I know," I said, promising myself that I would do everything I could to be nice to Serena in the future. I felt deeply ashamed of my former churlishness.

We got back to Pool Cottage. Serena insisted on seeing me right to the stable yard. I invited her in for a coffee, but she declined politely and said she had to return to the riding school. I watched her retreating back as she trotted down the road. There was no denying that she was a competent rider and a very good-hearted person.

| 8 |

Chapter Eight – Chatton Show

I woke on the morning of Chatton Show and rushed to the window. Today the weather was of utmost importance. Perhaps it was even a matter of life and death. For if it stormed again then Skydiver might bolt and we would kill not only oodles of innocent show-goers, but also ourselves. I imagined Mummy and Richard standing around my grave with tragic faces and little Hamish, not understanding that he would never know his big sister. As you can see, my experience yesterday seemed to have somewhat unhinged me and cast a huge maudlin shadow over my state of mind.

But my fears dissolved as I looked up into the sky and saw that it was a lovely blue, flecked with small white clouds. This was to be the peak of my childhood dreams, riding on my self-trained horse in the open jumping competition. Performing on Skydiver in a dressage exhibition would be fun, but not quite the same thing. I feared a little that it would be seen as swanking. No doubt, Susan King would be on hand to try and take the gloss off it. She would be eaten up with envy that I was the centre of attention.

I had packed up the horse box the night before, and we set off on the very short drive. I got there early and nabbed a good parking spot in the small field adjacent to the show ring. Everyone seemed to know me, and they waved and shouted morning greetings. I unloaded the horses and set them up with hay nets and buckets of water and decided to walk around to chat to people. I put some buckets on the ground beside the horse box, marking out a parking spot for Henry's old Land Rover. He and Ann were coming down later.

There was no great hurry to get the horses ready as I was giving the dressage exhibition at lunchtime, and the open jumping was halfway through the afternoon. I was in a sunny, happy mood, enjoying some nostalgia thinking of all the Chatton Shows I had attended over the years. Then a mighty black blast from the past.

"Good morning Jill!" said the unmistakable voice of Susan Pyke-now-King.

"Good morning Susan," I replied in an even, neutral tone, determined not to get myself into a tizz over her comments which would undoubtedly be intended to annoy me.

"I'm looking forward to seeing your dressage exhibition," she said in a tinselly voice, tinged with unmistakable mockery. Undoubtedly, she was hoping I would make a fool of myself.

"Yes, it's my latest thing," I said, hoping to pass it off as a fad, not letting her know that I was dreaming of riding in the Olympics.

"I'm commentating," she said smugly. My heart sank. No matter how brilliantly we were going to perform, she was sure to be mean. Perhaps she was going to mock me publicly. I walked on, debating whether I should talk to Colonel Mottley and ask him to at least help with the commentating, just to keep a check on any flights of spite that Susan might indulge in. I continued my walk calling out to friends and acquaintances, but the shine had come off the day for me. I went back to the horse box and decided to ride Balius around, so he didn't get bored tied up for hours on end. Ann and Henry had arrived.

"You'll never guess, that blasted Susan King is commentating on my dressage exhibition," I told them gloomily.

"Oh, bad luck," said Ann. "But if you're brilliant, she can't wreck it up, or she'll look a fool."

"Never underestimate The Susan," I said, frowning. "Anyway, I'm going to ride Balius around a bit, let him get used to his surroundings, watch a few classes from the ringside. Then I'll come back and get changed to ride Skydiver."

"I can plait him up for you," said Ann.

"You're an absolute angel," I replied thankfully.

Balius felt very eager and interested in all the different people and horses, the smell of crushed grass, the crackling of the loudspeaker, and the coloured bunting flapping in the fresh summer breeze. We stood and watched some fat shiny cattle parading around the centre ring. I went over to the exercise arena where there were a bunch of children flying around, leaping over the practice fence with a couple of harassed looking mothers putting it back up each time it was knocked over.

I got back to the horse box, and Skydiver was all polished and primped ready for our exhibition.

"He looks a million dollars!" I exclaimed.

I unsaddled Balius and settled him back down to his hay net and mounted my dazzling and glamorous dressage horse.

"The whole horse world is going to be eaten up with jealousy at the sight of you on that horse," said Ann smiling at me. "Go and enjoy showing off!"

"I'm not showing off," I snapped at her. "I'm giving a demonstration to promote the noble cause of good horsemanship and the fine art of dressage.

"Of course, you are," said Ann soothingly.

Colonel Mottley had arranged for the music to be played over the loudspeaker. I rode into the arena, and I could hear Susan's silken tones introducing me.

"Now we have little Jill Crewe, who has been competing at Chatton Show for many years. She is going to give us a demonstration of dressage on her new horse Skydiver."

We cantered slowly around the outside of the arena. I smiled at the crowd and was tempted to wave at them, as if I were Her Majesty. Then the first chords of the music struck up, and I began the routine that we had been practising for so many days.

A collected canter, and a collected trot, that then became a piaffe.

"This movement is called the piaffe and involves trotting on the spot," said Susan, speaking over the music.

Then we moved into an extended trot which as you will probably know looks absolutely splendid as if one is floating across the ground.

"This is an extended trot," said Susan.

Then a lateral movement, trotting in a diagonal across the arena, and diagonally back. I found my mind slipping into an altered state of consciousness, perhaps how one feels when smoking marijuana, but it was as if music, art and dance were flowing into one another.

"The diagonal movement is called a half-pass," said Susan. I was quite impressed in that tiny corner of my mind that wasn't concentrated on doing the performance. Susan was keeping it simple and accurate. Colonel Mottley had probably written her out a bit of a script.

Then, I was about to attempt the most difficult of the movements, the one-tempi changes. I gave Skydiver the correct aids, and then for a moment, my concentration was broken. There was a squawk over the loudspeaker. Then a strange high-pitched giggle. I put my mind back to the difficult canter movement. Out of the corner of my eye, I could see the audience was restless. There were ripples of laughter. Surely it wasn't our performance they were laughing at?

I got to the end of the one-tempi changes, and the music changed beat. We slowed down to a collected walk, then straight into a collected canter and two pirouettes and then a difficult transition into an extended canter, then back to collection and half-passes at canter. I had decided to try something very technically difficult, two-tempi changes on a diagonal. I knew that this was probably far beyond my ability, but I had thought I would give it a go in this setting, as my formal dressage career was going to have to carry on at a much lower level.

"Oh, Barty!" came Susan's voice floating over the loudspeaker. "You are naughty. Oh! That tickles!"

I didn't know whether to laugh or cry. Susan was obviously enjoying a conjugal moment with her new husband. Was she trying to ruin my exhibition? Surely not. I saw Colonel Mottley sprinting towards the little box that stood about six feet above the ground, which gave the person on the loudspeaker a good view of the ring.

I maintained my collected walk. I suspected that no-one was watching me anymore. They were tittering and pointing. Hopefully, Colonel Mottley would restore order, turn up the music, and I would pick up the movements. As the end of the piece of music was supposed to coincide with the end of the exhibition, I would have to cut it short. I kept one eye on Colonel Mottley, who was now at the door of the little wooden room. I prepared for the turns on the haunches. Presumably, Susan and Barty would no longer be cavorting together!

We did a couple of slightly wonky turns on the haunches. I set off at a collected canter diagonally across the arena. I could hear the music was about to come to an end and I cut short our planned routine. We halted in the centre of the arena. We did a quarter turn, and I bowed to the crowd, another quarter turn and another bow and then another. There was a splatter of applause, but the spectators had been distracted. I patted Skydiver. As usual, he had done well. At least there had been no thunder and lightning.

I rode out. Ann was standing waiting for me.

"Oh well done Jill! That was brilliant. You wowed them!" she cried.

"No, I didn't. Susan ruined it with her stupid carry-on. What was that about?" I asked plaintively.

"Jill! I thought you would find it amusing. She's made a complete idiot of herself," said Ann, a mischievous smile playing around her lips.

"Yes, but it was also at my expense," I said.

"Come on, Jill, it was a bit of fun at our local show. People will remember you, and Skydiver as well as Susan and the Insatiable Barty."

"Do you and Henry behave like that?" I asked desperately.

Ann didn't reply immediately.

"If we do, it is certainly in private," she replied primly.

"Sorry, that was a stupid thing to say, I'm just upset."

"Jill come on. You've still got the open jumping on Balius. It's not like you were humiliated. You've got to buck up. I thought you would find it hilarious."

I sniffed a couple of times and slid off Skydiver. We led him back to the horse box.

"Well done! That was amazing!" said a teenage girl, who was standing there watching me.

"Jolly good Jill!" called out the raucous voice of April Cholly-Sawcutt. "You're obviously soaring up the ladder in the dressage field!"

This cheered me up a bit. Although, I suspected that April was being facetious.

"Are you in the open jumping this afternoon. You know you'll be up against my Gary!" she called.

"Then I haven't a hope," I retorted, suddenly filled with determination that no matter what we would get a clear round.

We got back to the truck, and I nearly fell over with surprise. It was Martin Lowe being pushed in his wheelchair by his father. Martin had taught me to ride when I had first got Black Boy and had been utterly clueless.

"Well, young Jill, you've certainly come on apace," he said, smiling at me proudly.

"You were my teacher," I replied humbly.

"I thought you were living up in the wilds of Scotland with your mother and her new husband."

"I've been coming back down to Chatton now and again. Did you know that Mummy has had a baby boy, called Hamish?"

Just for a moment, Martin looked shocked and wistful. Then he rallied.

"How exciting! You must give me the address, and I can send a letter of congratulation."

For just a moment, it dawned on me that Martin might have been more than a little fond of my mother, but being in a wheelchair, he had probably thought he had nothing to offer. I suddenly felt like the happy enclosed world of my childhood was being chipped away with all these revelations.

Henry came striding over, his leather bag in his hand.

"How was that chestnut then, was it colic?" asked Ann.

"Just a touch of indigestion. I gave him some medicine, and they're walking him around. Hopefully, it'll pass," he said grinning.

"Well Jill, obviously the sight of a dancing horse can be something of an aphrodisiac!"

"Don't lay that at my door. Nothing to do with me!" I retorted.

"Poor old Susie, she won't be holding her head up for some time, I imagine," he said.

"Henry, do you know Martin Lowe?" I asked.

"I heard there was a new vet come to Chatton," said Martin holding out his hand for a firm handshake.

"Let's go and watch the under-sixteen jumping," said Ann. "We can remember our palmy days when we were eager young girls."

I walked beside her. I felt as if I needed to straighten out my thoughts. The showjumping - that was what was important. All my life, I had envisaged competing in the open jumping competition at Chatton. I wanted to look at the course and see what they had come up with this year. It looked much the same as every other year. The familiar old red wall that had received a fresh coat of paint, the triple bar painted orange and green, the plank fence with its bright design of red and white diamonds.

I recognised some of the students from Mrs Darcy's riding school. Serena and Wendy were in the collecting ring, checking stirrup lengths and tightening girths. The students looked very competent, and I hoped that they would do well. We watched a few rounds and then Clemmie Anderson, one of the star students riding Jackinabox jumped clear. Ann and I cheered and clapped. There were six clear rounds, and they set up the jump-off course. Clemmie went clear again, but she wasn't as fast as a tough-looking boy called Bobby Johnston who was riding a cob with a hogged mane called Bratton Boy.

"It's the novice horse class next, then the open. Do you think you should get ready now?" suggested Ann.

"Yes, you're right," I said. I sprinted back to the horse box and tacked up. Then, I brushed out Balius's mane and tail. I went into the back of the horse box and put on my blue riding jacket and matching blue velvet cap and gave my boots a bit of a polish. Balius was stamping his hoof impatiently, as if to say, 'come on hurry up, we've got a competition to win'.

I mounted, and we walked over to the ring. They were re-arranging the course for the novice event. I walked in a wide circle around to the other side of the arena. Balius had settled now, having spent the whole day here he had become accustomed to the noise and the other horses and riders. He walked out confidently, and I felt truly at one with him. We knew each other so well. I was filled with quiet confidence. This was to be the culmination of all my childhood dreams, to be jumping in the open event at Chatton Show on a horse I had trained myself. As long as we scored a clear round, I would be content. I would feel as if I had arrived. Certainly, it wasn't the dressage event at the Olympics, but a real tangible dream that was well within my grasp.

I saw the other riders going into the arena to walk the course. There was Gary Horton, with April hanging off his arm, chattering away. He almost shook her off at one point, and again I wondered about their relationship. Obviously, April's father's showjumping yard was a major advantage to the ambitious Gary. I hoped that when I did finally get a boyfriend, it would be straightforward and not tangled up with some form of social or material exchange that might be added into the equation. I began to fantasise about Jack and myself. We would love each other for our sweet souls, sharing our love for horses together. If anything, it would be me taking advantage of his expertise and contacts in the horse world.

It wasn't Gary Horton who won the novice horse competition, but rather Frank Stabley, who had been competing and winning at Chatton Show since I was thirteen. Gary was glowering at Frank, obviously upset that he had been beaten. But Frank was happily oblivious. He grinned at the judges as he was presented with a small trophy and waved it above his head as he galloped around the ring. He was local, and a great favourite and the crowd cheered enthusiastically.

The helpers rushed into the ring and re-arranged the jumps, and there were a bunch of us to walk the course. I found myself in step with Frank who I had known since the days of *Jill's gymkhana*.

"You've proved yourself quite a horsewoman," he said to me admiringly, his brown eyes twinkling.

"Thank you, Frank," I said, grinning back at him.

"I remember when you got the only clear round on Black Boy all those years ago. I think you must have been thirteen."

"You remember that!" I exclaimed. Of course, *I* remembered it. It had been my first moment of pure triumph, and one never forgets things like that.

"How about we go out to dinner and talk about old times," he said to me.

I opened my mouth, but no words came out.

"Obviously, you're overcome with excitement at the notion of sharing a meal with me," he laughed in a lovely jolly sort of way.

"That would be fun," I said. "I'm indulging in a lot of nostalgic reminisces lately."

"Are you still at Pool Cottage?" he asked.

"Yes."

"Well, what if I swing by tomorrow night, pick you up at seven."

He was taking charge in a very manly manner.

"Yes," I gasped, rather carried away. For some bizarre reason, I felt as if I were being unfaithful to Jack, which was ridiculous as Jack and I were only an item in my imagination.

"Let's pace this out," he said to me. "The distance between the wall and the gate looks a bit tricky to me."

He was right. It was five long, or six short strides.

"My chap is a big thoroughbred, he'll do five long strides here," said Bob.

"Balius has got pony breeding, so we'll go for the six short strides," I said, going back to step it out again.

The stewards ordered us off the course. They called out the first three numbers to get ready to jump. I was to go sixth, and Frank was seventh. Ann was holding Balius's reins and gave me a leg up to mount. I jumped the practice jump a few times. Frank was trotting around on a big chestnut thoroughbred that was at least 17 hh.

"He's a very impressive-looking horse," I called to him as he swept past us.

"Yours looks like a useful jumper," said Frank.

Frank had been right about the distance between the wall and the gate. Not only was the striding tricky, but the line between them was subtly curved. I would have to make sure that we landed on the left leg. After the gate, there was a sharp turn to the right, and it was necessary to pick up speed for a wide triple bar. The first two riders hit the gate and then failed to turn sharply enough and were too slow at the triple bringing that down as well. The third rider just managed it, but the effort must have been too great, and they hit the last jump, a deceptively simple, straight fence that had to be treated carefully just when one might have felt like rushing through the finish.

I cantered Balius around asking for more collection, then pushing him on to longer strides and then a turn to the left and over the practice jump. He felt good beneath me, and somehow, I knew that we were going to go clear. It was as if the stars were aligned especially for our success today. Frank had reminded me that Chatton Show was where it had all begun for me, and somehow, this was a lucky omen.

I heard the loudspeaker announcing that the last two riders had eight faults each. This was good, too many clear rounds indicated that the course was too easy. I was utterly determined that we would go clear and that Balius's canny pony instincts would make sure that we twisted and turned at the right moments.

I rode into the ring, and we jumped the first brush jump as if it were nothing. I knew then that everything was going to be good. We forged on to the double, pop, two strides, pop over the second element. Then we were heading towards the wall. I collected Balius with his hindquarters underneath him, so he was bouncing like a ball. He took off, and we were up and over, landing on the left leg, I counted out loud and then there was the gate, and we were clear. A sharp turn right and I pushed him on to go faster, he took off, and we soared over the wide triple. With just one more fence, I made sure I didn't throw it all away and held him together as we approached the straight jump. We soared over it and galloped with a flourish through the finish. We had gone clear. My grin stretched across my face, and I patted Balius, who shook his head as if to say, 'not a problem'.

"Well done!" called Frank as he cantered into the ring as I exited.

"Good luck!" I called back to him.

But he didn't go clear. He had the second part of the double down. Not even a problem fence. So far, I was the only clear round. But there was still Gary Horton to go. He galloped into the ring on a very handsome chocolate-brown gelding. They were leaping around the jumps as if they were tiny. I was sure they would go clear, and I think Gary thought the same. Right up until the last jump, and he was too cocky, and he was going too fast. His horse clipped the top rail. I think everyone watching held their breath. It rocked in its cups and then slowly, slowly toppled to the ground. I wanted to cheer out loud but managed to clap my hand over my mouth. It would have been such bad form.

As the last rider rode out of the ring with a whopping sixteen faults, I knew that I was the winner. I couldn't believe it. We had won the open jumping at Chatton Show. I rode up to the judges and was presented with a giant cup, a big blue rosette, a certificate and an envelope with my lovely winnings – all to be spent on Balius. He was the most wonderful chap. I was determined that he would never be eclipsed in my affections.

"Gary Horton and Frank Stabley have agreed to share second place," came over the loudspeaker. We cantered in a lively procession around the outside of the arena. The crowd were cheering wildly. This was what it felt to be a popular winner!

I was still floating on a happy cloud the next day. Both Balius and Skydiver had the day in the field together. The weather was very hot, and I spent the day lying on a rug in the garden, reading a frivolous book *Apricot Sky* by Ruby Ferguson. I loved the jokey, casual style, and I got caught up in the love affair. I was still dreaming of Jack, the elegant, debonair international dressage rider. I didn't give much thought to going out that evening with Frank. It was merely a matter of catching up with an old friend. I even suggested to Ann that she and Henry come along.

"Jill, I think that Frank meant it to be a date. You know *a date!*"

I looked at her in surprise.

"No, I don't think so, it's just catching up."

"Jill you're a total dope sometimes, you just don't seem to be able to grasp the nettle!"

"It's not like that at all!" I retorted.

Having stood my ground, I now had to follow through. Again, that awkward issue of what to wear? I began to think that it might be easier to go out to a department store and buy up a dozen outfits that would suit every occasion. In the end, I chose a bright summer frock, white with large red blooms, and a thin black belt, worn with flat black shoes.

"Now that is lovely!" said Ann approvingly. "You look extremely fetching! In fact, I would say you are Allure Abundant!"

"Fetching! Allure!" I snorted inelegantly and nearly dashed back upstairs to change. But the arrival of Frank meant that I had to greet him, and then he whisked me away. Ann couldn't help herself and threw a final, whispered comment at me as I went through the door.

"You two are going to click together like two halves of a pair of scissors," she said mischievously. I went bright red, matching the floral design on my dress and hoped that Frank had not heard this sally.

"I thought we might go into Rychester to that pizza restaurant. It's not grand, but I rather like the different flavours," said Frank.

"Sounds delish," I said, glad that this was setting the tone for the dinner, cheap, cheerful and friendly. Not grand. Nothing intimidating and weird.

We each ordered two different flavours, so there were a total of four different combinations.

"Ann would love this. She's trying to create different flavour combinations. She's talking about writing a cookery book," I commented.

"What about your writing?" he asked. "How is that going?"

I was rather pleased that he was interested in me and knew about my life. He wasn't big-headed and egotistical just talking about himself. I reeled off the names of my pony books, but then started to tell him about my latest efforts writing for *Horse and Hound*. He looked extremely impressed and said that he did vaguely remember reading the article about the sisters who rode their ponies through London, but he hadn't noticed the name of the writer.

After we had exhausted this topic, I had wanted to ask him about himself. I realised that I knew very little about him, but before I could open my mouth to ask the question, he had changed the topic to my life in Scotland. There was so much to tell about the castle, the grouse shooting, the cross-country course and I found it hard to eat the pizza. Eventually, I managed to change the subject. I asked him about Gary Horton. Now it was his turn to wax lyrical, if that is what you call salacious gossip. I had always thought that such chatter about one's friends and not-so-friends was the province of women, but now I found that men were just as good at telling stories about others.

"Gary is certainly one for the girls," he said. "They say he has enjoyed any number of liaisons with the staff at the yard."

I was shocked at this.

"You mean before he and April got together," I said.

Frank smiled at me.

"You do like to think the best of people, don't you," he said. I pondered this. Was he saying I was a nice person, or that I was naïve? I certainly didn't like the idea of April being betrayed when it was apparent she was madly in love with her fiancé.

"Don't worry. I think April has his measure. She keeps him on a short leash," said Frank.

I felt depressed at this. I must be the most inexperienced person when it came to relationships, but the thought that April had mastered the art was indeed off-putting.

"I would hate it to be like that for me," I said. "I would want to trust my boyfriend, or husband, and not have to be watching them like a hawk."

"Good on you," said Frank smiling warmly at me.

I decided that this was getting too close to the bone. I began to talk about Val and Jackie Heath. He knew all about Val's trip to America. He even knew the family she was staying with. I was fascinated to find out about the opportunities in Virginia where apparently, they were awfully impressed by British accents and assumed that we were all friends of the Royal family.

"I'm going back to Porlock Vale to do my Assistant Instructor's Certificate," I confided.

"Wow! They really would love you in America with that," he said. "They'll have you training their Olympic team."

It was on the tip of my tongue to tell him my plans to get chosen for the British Olympic Team, but I couldn't quite bring myself to trust him that much. I asked him about Dinah Dean, but he'd heard nothing about her, or Mercy Dulbottle. Then I asked about Saintly Serena.

"I know her quite well. We were going out for a while," he said quietly.

"You were going out with Serena," I exclaimed. This made me feel very weird. It was like my old world of Chatton wasn't quite as I remembered it. We were growing up. Alliances shifting. New connections evolving.

"She is a really nice woman, but we just weren't that well suited. She's not ambitious. She's happy to be a riding school teacher. She has no aspirations to compete at a top-level," he explained. "I'm looking for someone who shares my ambitions."

This silenced me. I chewed furiously on a piece of pizza, which was piled with mozzarella, sliced ham and red peppers.

"What do you do?" I asked. "Are you just riding, or pursuing some other form of employment?"

"I'm lucky. You know my father is a farmer. He is happy for me to have a stable full of horses, and I help him out on the farm in return, so I don't have to go to work in an office or anything. If it doesn't work out with the horses, then I guess I'll just take over the farm."

He called over to the waitress and asked if there was a dessert menu. We both decided on gelato ice-cream. At the end of the evening, he drove me home, and as we drew up to Pool Cottage I asked him to come in for coffee. I knew that Ann would be around, so I wasn't worried about any embarrassing moments with just the two of us.

Ann brought out a bottle of red wine and poured us each a generous glass. We settled down to more delicious local gossip. Ann had quite a few juicy details to contribute, which she had gleaned from Henry's work as the local vet. We all laughed uproariously at the thought of Clarissa Dandleby and her ancient fiancé. Then we began to act out the whole Susan and Barty episode while I was doing my dressage exhibition. It suddenly became hilarious, and I saw the funny side that had rather evaded me at the time.

Finally, Frank got up reluctantly, and I saw him to the door. He gave me a peck on the cheek, and we promised each other we would meet up again next time I came to Chatton. For tomorrow I was off to Scotland, then down to Exmoor and back to Scotland for Christmas.

"You two seemed to get on well," said Ann smugly.

"And why shouldn't we?" I flung back at her and rushed up the stairs to bed.

Now you might think that I lay in bed and thought about Frank and all we had talked about. Perhaps I might even have come to the imminently sensible conclusion that someone like Frank, from my home town, would be a much more suitable match than Jack Laskey!

But instead, I lay there and thought about Susan Pyke, now Susan King. She had always been important in my life, like 'point and counterpoint'. Somehow, I imagined that we had a sort of grudging respect for each other – perhaps what you can only get between sworn enemies. She had married a local from the small pool of possibles and seemed to be glorying in her married state. It wasn't as if she would grow into a shabby middle-aged woman getting on and off a bus, all varicose veins and pincurls. She would be Smart and Social and have a select circle of cronies, just like at school. Perhaps, I would still be flitting around from pillar to post chasing horse dreams.

| 9 |

Chapter Nine – Bagpipes at Dawn

On my first morning back at the castle I leapt out of bed and went to the window, as weather-wise people do, especially in the Highlands when the weather often determined the course of one's day. I had planned a long ride down to the sea on Balius. Whenever I had been away, I felt the need to clear the cobwebs and let the fresh Highland breeze blow through my mind and help me to think more clearly. And at the moment, I had a lot to think about!

The mountains in the distance were hazy, their purple-amethyst tops wreathed in strands of fairy-cotton mist, which is a sign of a bright, sunny day. When you can see the mountains clearly, it means it is going to rain, which shows you what a topsy-turvy world it is up here in Scotland.

It had been a long drive yesterday, and I wanted to get myself and Balius out into the bracing Highland air. I was sure that he would be happy to be back in his homeland.

I went down to the stables before I had breakfast and put Skydiver out in one of the small stone-walled fields that bordered the moorland. I thought he might enjoy the view and the sweet summer grass. He had Bonnie, Balius's mother in the field next to him. I told Hugh that I was planning a long ride on Balius and would be back in an hour or two to tack him up.

I asked Hugh if Mark was around. I didn't trust my step-cousin, and I certainly didn't want him doing anything to Skydiver. You might think that I was being ridiculously paranoid but when Mummy and I had first come to live at Blainstock and Richard had given me Balius as a gift, Mark had done his best to wreck him before I had even started breaking him in. It had taken me months to rectify the issues that Mark had created with my horse. Since then, I didn't like to leave any of my horses at Blainstock. If I was going away without them, then I took them down to Linda MacNally's. She was a brilliant rider, and I trusted her completely. Any training she did was sure to be better than what I could do myself.

"He's taken most of the competition horses down to Yorkshire for the summer. He's staying at Diana's place and riding around the shows. Apparently, according to Richard, he was at the International Horse Show at White City, and he met the Queen."

"What would he be doing there? Surely he's not entered the showjumping?" I asked incredulously.

"He took most of the horses to the Brickett Wood combined training event, which is run in conjunction with the big horse show, but he and Miss Barton-Tompkin are hobnobbing at the show as well."

"Good for them," I said tersely.

Anything to do with Mark set my hackles up. I had never forgiven him for what he had done to Balius, but I'd also overheard him refer to my mother as a gold-digger. That was utterly unforgivable!

"As long as he doesn't touch Skydiver. You know if he swans in and tries you will stop him, won't you Hugh?"

"Yes, Miss. I know the score, and Richard has told me how things stand."

I felt much happier that Mark was not around. I was looking forward to my day out with Balius. I went back to the castle for breakfast. It wouldn't be the sumptuous banquet that was served every morning when we had paying guests, but Cook always produced something substantial and delicious. Mummy was in the kitchen with baby Hamish, spooning what looked like thin gruel into his mouth.

"Is he eating porridge already?" I asked. Really, I didn't have a clue what babies ate.

"He is such a chubby, happy, little thing he's gone onto solids quite early. He loves eating off a spoon. He is very advanced, you know," she replied, her eyes shining with pride.

"Did you talk about me every minute of the day when I was a baby?" I asked. I was amazed that I didn't feel envious in the slightest. How odd that I should suffer the worst of poisonous-green jealousy when it came to Serena and her certificate, but sibling rivalry seemed to have entirely passed me by.

"Oh no, I've become one of those parents who is a total bore, talking about my children constantly. I've descended into utter banality! I don't think I did talk about you so much, you see it was very ordinary having a child in those days, it was what young couples did. I suppose I talked to other mothers, and we did discuss our babies. But you see, Jill, I never thought I would have another child. My life really did take such a surprising turn!"

"I know, I wasn't being mean," I hastily assured her. "I do think he's gorgeous and you can talk about him as much as you want to me, and of course Richard."

"Richard is totally thrilled to have an heir, you see," said Mummy. "I think he had entirely given up on the idea. It's given him a new lease of life."

I smiled at her benignly. I was truly happy for them. They were such good people they deserved all the happiness in the world.

"Actually, we have a rather exciting new thing happening, we've got some locals coming in every Thursday evening, after dinner, to give a demonstration of sword-dancing, and then the guests can have a go themselves."

"Gosh, I hope they don't skewer themselves, it would be rather unfortunate to slice our paying guests down the middle!" I exclaimed.

"Don't be silly, Jill. The swords are placed flat on the floor, not stuck into the ground with them leaping over the upright blades. It's all rather good fun. They wear these wonderful tartan-patterned socks with matching kilts, and they leap about with their arms in the air. Richard is determined to become more Scottish than the Scottish themselves. I think it's something to do with having produced an heir. We all have to shout 'slainte', the Scottish toast when we have a drink. He's even started using Scottish words such as 'brae' and 'whins', and I have to ask him for a translation."

"Little Hamish is going to grow up as an iconic Highland man. Anyway, what is a 'brae', isn't that a hill? But I have no idea what a 'whins' is?"

"A brae is a hill or a slope, and the whins are spiky bushes such as gorse."

"I noticed that you seem to be living in tartan trews," I commented, "I think you've worn them every day since I've been here."

"Actually, I have several pairs, and the pattern is slightly different," replied Mummy loftily. "But it *is* interesting that you're beginning to take an interest in clothes now?" she commented, in that tone that was leading up to something along the lines of a mother and daughter talk.

"He'll have us all believing in fairies soon," I joked, desperate to change the subject. Mummy gave me a look, and I wondered if she had in fact been persuaded that fairies did exist. We were both silent for a moment. I looked over at the rosy-cheeked little Hamish. He was rather adorable. I wondered whether Jack wanted children.

"Why don't we think about a games room as well, for the guests?" I suggested. "I'm sure there's some fabulous Scottish games but also the old favourites, darts, quoits, skittles, or even an indoor obstacle course for the children and things like that. It's not like we don't have the space."

"What a brilliant suggestion, Jill – you have such an original mind! I must talk to Richard. He was saying only the other day that we need to provide the guests with more entertainment. The traditional house party is just not enough these days, people seem to need more things to entertain them," said Mummy.

"The curse of the modern age," I muttered darkly.

I went down to saddle Balius and found that John had saddled up one of the three young horses that Mark had had broken in and left behind.

"Wow! You've graduated to riding Mark's young horses!" I exclaimed.

He grinned at me.

"Can I come with you on a ride? This one could do with another horse to show him what good manners are."

"Of course," I said. Although I had thought I needed some thinking time, it would be more fun to have company. We set off up the lane towards the moor.

"It must be quiet with Mark away," I said, just making idle conversation.

"That's the problem," said John.

"What do you mean?" I asked.

"There's not much work to do. We're wondering what's going to happen."

"What!" I exclaimed in sudden shock.

"Most of the work was Mark's horses. I mean Richard had Bonnie and Balius, and there's a couple of other ones that are used with the shooting. We thought that with your horses as well we'd be busy. But you're taking them away quite a lot."

"Gosh!" I said. "I never really thought about it. I just came here, and there were all these amazing facilities and Mark the ambitious eventer. I took it all for granted."

A pair of partridges leapt out from under Balius's hoofs with a whirr and clatter of wings, crying a harsh 'klark' of alarm. The young horse John was riding leapt into the air with fright.

"The other stable staff have gone now. There's just Hugh and me, but there's hardly enough work even for the two of us. That's one of the reasons why I'm riding this horse and Hugh is helping with the shoot-ing guests. But it's a bit unsettling," replied John.

We'd got to the moorland now and were following a wide track that would lead around the loch and then we would turn off over the hills towards the sea.

"I thought I might ride to the sea, but perhaps that young one won't be up for it?" I suggested.

"It might be a bit far for him," conceded John. "He's not that fit yet. His muscles are still getting accustomed to being ridden, especially over rough ground."

We trotted on. Again, I noticed what a good rider John was.

"Don't you want to do something with your riding, compete, show the world what you can do?" I asked.

"I leave that to you and Mark," he replied with a grin. I didn't like be-ing bracketed with Mark, but he did have a point. We headed through the hills and began to climb upwards. Finally, we stopped and gave the horses a rest, sitting high on a turf-clad hill. We could see down to the sea where dirty-cream sands and the rollers met in a thunder of spray. Hundreds of gulls were perched on the rocks below. Out on the sea, thousands of birds bobbed on the swell and dived with a flash of wings. When they rose, their cries were flung high on the wind and contributed to the sea symphony. Huge clouds rolled in the blue sky, taking the shape of the islands below them. The air was scented by the sea, turf and heather.

We stood and gazed. The minutes slipped by.

"That's as far as this one should go," said John.

"I'll come back with you," I replied. "This view of the sea is enough. I feel like I'm truly back in Scotland now."

"It's enough for me," said John, perhaps referring back to my com-ment about wanting to compete.

The next day I rode out with John again. I asked him to ride Balius. I wanted to see him jump around some of the cross-country jumps. I was determined that John should start training to compete. He might say he didn't want to, but I thought he was so good it would be a waste for him to be a humble groom all his life. I rode Skydiver. The long journey from Oxford to the Highlands seemed to have done him no harm. He was stepping out with a little more enthusiasm than normal. Perhaps he liked the invigorating Scottish air.

"I thought we might go around the cross-country course today," I said.

"Certainly," assented John.

He looked good on Balius. He rode with accomplished ease. We walked around for twenty minutes. Then, I set off trotting up the hill and across the top of the field. I was more interested in Balius than Skydiver.

"We'll trot down the far slope. Then we can head up the hill, I'll go in front of you, to the side of the jumps and you can have a go at them," I said in what was probably a bossy tone. I was so busy looking over my shoulder to see how John sat a horse over a jump that I was totally unprepared for what happened next. I'd trotted to the left of the first log fence and then on to past a simple post-and-rails. I probably wasn't steering straight, as the next thing that happened was Skydiver headed straight for the steps up the hill. There were three of them, each three feet high and then he went straight over a post-and-rail at the top that was easily three foot six. I hung on by my fingernails, nearly tipping off backwards. John came steaming up behind me.

"He jumps well," he commented as if it were the most natural thing in the world.

"He's a dressage horse. He doesn't jump at all," I barked.

"Tell him that then," said John with a wide grin.

We pulled up, and I got my breath back.

"He looked like a natural to me," said John. "Come on, let's do some more. I love jumping this chap. He's fantastic!"

Automatically, I wanted to say 'no, no, no'! But then curiosity overcame my preconceptions. What if Skydiver could jump, like jump really well, like jump to the top of the showjumping world!

"Let's go over that tabletop thing," said John. "I'll give you a lead if you're nervous!"

"I'm not nervous!" I retorted.

We both set off at a fair clip, what one would call a good hunting pace, and Balius surged ahead with John urging him on. The jump was easily four feet high and probably five feet across. Balius leapt, and I could see him straining a bit to make it. Skydiver didn't hesitate for a second. He soared into the air, like a bird flying. He had more natural ability than any horse I'd ever ridden, including Mrs Darcy's novice Messmate who I had jumped in the Grade C at Chatton Show a few years ago.

"It's not right. He's worth about two thousand pounds for doing brilliant dressage," I gasped when we pulled up.

"Well maybe he's worth even more as he can jump *and* do dressage!" said John, who really didn't seem to be taking me seriously.

I couldn't come up with any reply to this. I had to think. I had automatically decided that a valuable dressage horse shouldn't be wasting their legs on jumping, particularly fixed cross-country jumps. But if he was as brilliant at jumping, as he was at dressage, then he could be a top eventer. This was a major leap from my previous plan. I would have to think about this. Perhaps I should talk to Linda. She was one of the wisest people that I knew.

I was silent as we rode back down to the stables. John seemed oblivious of my state of mind. I wondered if life might be easier, if I could be as happy-go-lucky as him, keeping busy with honest toil. Hugh took Skydiver from me in the stable yard, and Linda came out of the office.

"Oh Linda, I was coming down to see you," I said, immediately brightening.

"I haven't seen you for yonks," she commented. "How did it go at Porlock Vale? Hugh was telling me you went there for a dressage course. And I read your piece about the Clattering Clutterbucks."

"Come inside. Let's get something to eat. I'm starving," I insisted, wanting Linda all to myself.

"You should see that fancy dressage horse jumping," said John guilelessly to Hugh.

"Really!" exclaimed Linda. "I didn't know he jumped as well."

"Come inside!" I demanded, grabbing her by the arm. "I *really* need to talk to you."

I was practically begging now. Linda turned to Hugh with her eyebrows raised, and he nodded at her. We went inside and straight down to the kitchen.

"Now you go into the scullery and wash your hands," said Cook bossily to me. I splashed around noisily in the big sink.

"Tea for you both," said Cook. "I'll make some sandwiches."

"So much to tell," I said but tucked into the sandwiches first. "But how is the riding school going?"

"Chugging along. Quite a few of the guests coming up to stay at the castle are interested in riding, so we should be busy for a few weeks," she replied.

"It's Skydiver. We did dressage at Porlock Vale then Jack Laskey rode him in an advanced dressage test at Tavistock, and he came first. Later, I took him in a test at Houghton, just really basic stuff, and he did brilliantly, twenty marks ahead of the competition. But now I'm going back to Porlock to do the Horsemasters course for fifteen weeks, to get the Assistant Instructor's Certificate but I can't take the horses."

"Do you want me to take them?" she asked. "I can't do that much with them with a full schedule of riders, but when they leave, I'll have plenty of time."

"If Mark stays away in Yorkshire they can be stabled at the castle and maybe you could just come and ride them here. But if Mark comes back, I don't want him interfering with them."

"He might not come back," she said a little hesitantly.

"Do you mean it's easier for him competing down south?" I asked.

"Perhaps," she said, but her eyes were swivelling evasively.

"What happened this morning. I was looking behind me, I wanted to see John jumping on Balius, and then Skydiver just leapt up the steps, you know those three upward jumps, and then over the post-and-rails at the top and then we took them both over that huge tabletop jump. I've never jumped a horse like it. He just soared as if it were nothing."

"Gosh," said Linda. I was relieved to see that she knew what this meant. "So, with his dressage, which is stupendous and also jumping, you might have yourself a top-flight eventing horse."

"Yes," I breathed.

"That is utterly fantastic. Lucky you!"

She was pleased for me, but I could hear the tinge of envy in her voice. And why not? It was a perfectly natural reaction. I would have felt the same. I was very conscious that Linda was a far better rider and trainer than me. By rights, it was her that deserved the luck of having a horse like Skydiver dropped in her lap.

"I didn't want to jump him because of him being so good at dressage," I said plaintively.

"Did he jump like he was trained, or just natural exuberance and *joie de vivre* out in the open," she asked.

"I don't know. I guess we should try him around the showjumps in the arena. Could you ride him for me, so you can tell me what you think?"

"Of course," she replied, smiling. "It will be my pleasure."

"Jill darling, you're back," said Mummy coming in with Hamish in her arms.

"Oh! Look, it's the wee baby," said Linda, cooing. Somehow, I didn't think of Linda as the sort of person to go all gooey over a baby.

We went down to the stables and tacked up Skydiver. Hugh, John and I followed Linda down to the indoor arena. We set up the jumps in a series of three, two strides, and three strides apart. Skydiver with Linda on his back leapt them like a professional. Then we changed the distances so that he had two long strides, and then three short strides and Linda managed to extend and shorten his stride perfectly.

"Do you think he's a top eventer who was stolen and then sold to Tatiana de Vere on the black market?" I asked. It seemed the likeliest explanation.

"Perhaps," said Hugh. "I guess if you start competing on him, then you'll find out. It might be that he's just a brilliant horse, a natural." He shrugged. I hoped desperately that we wouldn't find out that he was stolen.

"I have to think about this," I said.

"Do you want to jump him?" asked Linda.

"No, I think he's had enough for today," I said.

The next day the guests began to arrive. I was sucked into an endless cycle; being woken at daybreak by the sound of bagpipes, tending to the guests' needs, and then dressing up for the evening meal, joining in the convivial gatherings, being charming and friendly.

Linda had brought all her horses and ponies up to the castle and was using the facilities to offer proper lessons as well as treks around the loch and across the moorland. John and Hugh were helping her, and the guests were extremely enthusiastic. The problem of owning a horse that could be one of the top eventers in Britain, and probably Europe, was put on hold for quite a few weeks. I can imagine you saying dear readers, 'how can this be a problem?' and 'get a grip, Jill, and go for it'. I think the issue was that I didn't think I was worthy of such a wonderful horse. I had been worried that I wouldn't be good enough for him with a dressage career, but eventing was so much more difficult. What if I just didn't have it in me? I would fail him.

Even before the last guests left, I had to drive down to Exmoor. It seemed more important than ever that I should get some expert training. Skydiver would be better off with Linda and Hugh anyway. They were more than capable of looking after him. Before I left, I took a deep breath and suggested that Linda take him south for a few events when the horse trial season opened. She could go in the horse trailer with Hugh or John and perhaps enter Glanusk or Malton. If he really was going to be a superstar, then he needed some experience. I knew that Linda was the right rider for him. I could trust her to look after him.

| 10 |

Chapter Ten – Becoming A Horsemaster

I arrived back at Porlock Vale feeling rather foolish. The other Horsemasters would be travelling there by train or at least driving small cars or Land Rovers. I roared in at the wheel of my big empty horse box. There was a perfectly logical reason for this! After the course, I had to go down to Essex to get Copperplate who had been staying at the fearsome Tatiana's place. I parked at the back of the stables, but it was impossible to hide such a big vehicle!

This time at Porlock Vale I was staying at the other house, riding their school horses not my own. The idea was that we were all to ride different horses, and indeed some problematic ones to improve our riding skills. With no horses to unload, I made my way to the front entrance of the old Edwardian house. The door was standing open, so I knocked and called out.

"Come in, come in," snapped a woman, as if I shouldn't have to be told.

I was carrying a suitcase in each hand.

"Hello, I'm Jill Crewe, here for the Horsemasters' course," I said briskly, responding to her brusque business-like tone.

"Good, good. There's the list, tick yourself off and upstairs to your bedroom. They're all numbered. Stow your gear and then tea is in the sitting room at four this afternoon, and we'll make all the introductions," she said hurrying away, throwing the last sentence over her shoulder as she went.

This was entirely different to the greeting I had received as an Equitator, but I didn't mind. I was no grand lady who needed obsequious treatment. I ran my finger down the list and saw that I was sharing Room Five with a woman called Geraldine Royston. I hadn't thought of sharing, but it might be rather jolly, if she were a cheerful type. She hadn't ticked herself off so I guessed that I would have my choice of bed. It would be rather like boarding school, I imagined.

Room Five was a cheerful daffodil-yellow with green and blue curtains. It reminded me of my cousin Cecilia's yellow-embroidered napery, but it was better than something dismal grey or brown. The two beds were against the wall with the same view out of the large casement window that looked down into the garden and beyond the fields to the village that nestled on the edge of the bay.

I stowed my clothes into one of the wardrobes and half of the drawers of the large oak dresser. Checking the time, I realised that I had another hour and a half before tea. I couldn't resist. I would walk the half-mile down the road to the other house and see if I didn't just bump into Jack. Now I was here, my mind flooded with memories of him. None of my enthusiasm to pursue a friendship with him had waned.

I walked down the lane. The high hedges on either side of the road obscured the view, except at the gateways where you could either look down to the sea or up to the moorland. The stable yard was more or less empty. I guessed that there was no Equitator course running at the moment. One of the working pupils emerged from the tack room.

"Ruth!" I called, feeling a surge of relief as I recognised her. She was an enthusiastic and down-to-earth person. "How are you?"

She peered at me for a moment.

"Jill! I didn't recognise you. What are you doing here?"

"I'm on the Horsemasters' course this time," I said proudly as if stating my credentials.

"Jolly good! That's going to be a bit different than one of the ladies in the dressage class!" She laughed out loud as if she had made a terrific joke. I cackled along with her.

"How have things been going here?" I asked, hoping desperately for any crumb of news about Jack.

"It's been a good summer, lovely weather, we've taken some of the horses down to the beach, riding in the water, good for their legs," said Ruth in hearty tones.

I realised then that Ruth would have no clue of how to pass on any interesting, salacious or intriguing gossip. She was thoroughly horsey in every sense of the word. Only a few short weeks ago I would have approved of such a young woman. How things had changed with the advent of Jack into the fringes of my life.

"Who will be instructing us, in the Horsemasters' course?" I asked innocently.

"Captain Romanski, of course, for dressage, that's on Wednesday and Friday mornings. Colonel Whetton is the other three days, with some jumping both in the arena and of course the cross-country. Then Miss Follett in the afternoons for stable management and veterinary care."

"So, we don't have Jack Laskey at all?" I asked, my eyes purposefully round and innocent.

"Jack is usually for the Equitators, he likes to swan around with the great and the good," said Ruth, again laughing as if she had made a tremendous joke. I laughed along with her, albeit weakly.

"I'd better be getting back, it will be all meeting and greeting at tea," I replied, trying to hide a huge rush of disappointment. I had been banking on Jack being one of our instructors. What a miscalculation!

I marched back down the road. Surely at some point, my path would cross with Jack's. Even if it were only as one of the Horsemasters who had to act as grooms for the Equitators. As soon as he saw me, then we could pick up where we had left off.

By the time I got back to the house, it was bustling with the arrival of the other Horsemasters. At ten to four, we crowded into the living room and helped ourselves to tea or coffee and platefuls of sandwiches and cakes. Then we settled onto sofas, in armchairs, or on the carpet leaning against furniture. There were twelve of us.

The way things were run was explained very clearly by Colonel Whetton, who was in charge of the course. There would be two rides - the Blue and the Red. We were to take our lessons every weekday morning as one big ride, but our stable duties were divided, in that Thursday afternoon was a free half-day for one Ride and Saturday afternoon and Sunday was free time for the other. On Saturday morning we would all be taken for a hack up on the moor. In between looking after the school horses, we also had to muck in with the working pupils to help out with the Equitators. We all had tack cleaning as well as stable duties. And, we were expected to do private study so we could pass our stable management and veterinary care papers in the final exam. It was undoubtedly a punishing schedule. An examiner would come to the school to test us in the last few days of the course. We were exhorted to uphold the reputation of Porlock Vale as the best riding school in Britain, and it was stressed that our qualification would be recognised all over the world.

I thought that Colonel Whetton looked like a bucolic hunting type with his protruding and masterful nose and a clipped moustache that barely hid his large, yellow horse teeth. I hoped that he wasn't from the old school that insisted we lean well back over the jumps and chase us with a hunting stick if our horses looked like refusing. Surely not at Porlock Vale!

Captain Romanski was introduced to us. He looked at me and then smiled in recognition. At least he remembered me, or more likely he remembered Skydiver. Miss Follett was a formidable-looking woman with a large and noble Roman nose that jutted out of her face like a mountain crag.

Then, we had to introduce ourselves. They called out the names of the people in the Red Ride, and they shuffled up and stood in a line.

My name was not called, so obviously, I was in Blue. Each person was to address the room telling a little about him or herself and their ambitions once they gained the Certificate. I dreaded this, mostly as my pipe dream was to represent Britain in the Olympics. There was no way I could possibly admit to that!

I made a huge effort to remember the names of each of those who were introducing themselves. There were two young men and three young women and one older woman, who was perhaps forty years old.

The first of the young women stepped forward, she was rather hefty and certainly filled her baggy jodhpurs and large tweed hacking jacket.

"Good afternoon, my name is Georgie Beeston. I'm from Cheshire. I live on a farm with my parents. I've been riding all my life, and I work at the local riding school and will go back there with my Certificate. One day I hope to have my own riding school."

"Thank you, Miss Beeston, well said, succinct and to the point," said Colonel Whetton.

There was a hesitant round of applause from the rest of us. The next student stepped forward, a tall, lanky boy with very straight brown hair that was too long and hung over his eyes.

"Good afternoon, my name is Oswald Tettington-Ford, but at school, they used to call me Blubberbox, but I did once win a medal for elocution. My people live in Gloucestershire, and we run a livery stable. The idea is that I'm to start giving some riding lessons, so my father insisted that I get qualified."

I smiled a little at this. Oswald had the posh accent to go with his double-barrelled name. He looked rather like a string bean as if he hadn't done a hard day's work in his life. I found it extraordinary that he admitted to his nickname, which suggested that there would be tears before tea time as Nanny used to say.

The next was a diminutive, thin young girl who looked about twelve. She had a high-pitched flutey voice.

"Hello, I'm Etta, my real name is Henrietta Snook."

Everyone in the room laughed.

"I know, I know, who has a surname like Snook! I hate the Henrietta so you must call me Etta. I live in the suburbs in Basingstoke, and my parents don't know one end of a horse from another. I've finally persuaded them to let me come on this course, and I've had about four dozen riding lessons in my life. So I'm going to have to catch on very quickly." She grinned at us all. I thought, now she's got guts, to be mixing it with us, knowing some of us would have been riding all our lives. She was obviously devoted to horses and desperate to follow a career with them. I recited the three names to myself to try and remember; Georgie Beeston the hefty girl from farming stock, Oswald 'Blubberbox' the posho carrying on the family livery stable business, and sweet little Etta who was determined to make it as a rider and all-round good egg.

The next was the woman who I judged to be middle-aged. Now I know that as a still relatively young person I could call anyone over thirty-five 'old', but in the last few years I had grown up a lot, and I was determined not to write off anyone older than thirty as over the hill. After all, Jack must be at least as old as this woman, and I didn't think of him as old!

"Good afternoon, I'm Angela Cartwright. I've left my long-suffering husband at home with our three children so I can pursue my dream of becoming an equestrian professional. We have a happy-go-lucky family life, and it's not unknown for the horses to wander into the dining room and eat off the table, At the moment, I am a Pony Club mother but I want to do something for myself and not just be the unpaid groom and stable lad for my children."

Well good on you, Angela Cartwright, I thought to myself. I hoped that Mr Cartwright would appreciate her all the more when she returned to the family nest and he had discovered just how hard it was to look after three children.

The other young man now stepped forward.

"My name ees Pablo Rodriguez Camellia, I am from Espagna, and I love to ride the horses. I do a lot of showjumping, and my parents say that I must have some sort of education, so here I am." He bowed from the waist. A lot of the females in the room sighed. He was very handsome with his smooth dark skin, large liquid brown eyes and shiny black hair. I guessed he would be the Romeo of the course.

The last person of Red Ride stepped forward. She had been standing behind the others, looking shy. She was drop-dead gorgeous, with the most breath-taking beauty I had ever seen. She was from Sweden and epitomised the Aryan ideal that Hitler and his cronies had dreamed about. Instantly I knew that she was a rival who would just blast me out of the water in terms of looks.

In the past, I had always looked down on women who despised their rivals. I considered them to be witches who slunk about green with jealousy and grew into curdled old maids with gall dripping from their withered lips. I can imagine your eyes popping out as you read that last sentence and I admit I have poached it out of a book that Mummy was reading. In truth, I had never much thought about jealousy when it came to men. In my saner moments, I might have considered such sentiment proceeded from the unplumbed depths of vulgarity in one's nature. That was before I had become infatuated with the most gorgeous and desirable man in the world. Ariel Bergman was as cool as an icicle and beautiful as a waterfall. In comparison, I felt like a childish, over-heated, squashed-up tomato.

I managed to recover my *sang froid* and tried to memorise these last three; Angela Cartwright the housewife escapee, Pablo the Spanish Romeo and Ariel the unsurpassed Nordic beauty who was going to destroy any chance of me becoming Mrs Laskey.

The Red Ride went back to their seats: Georgie strode, Oswald minced, Etta tip-toed impishly, Mrs Cartwright swaggered, Pablo lounged, and Ariel was gliding like an angel. The rest of us got up and went to the front of the room as they read out our names. I found myself standing next to Geraldine Royston, my roommate, who was the first to introduce herself. She stepped forward, a curvaceous good-looking brunette. Do you notice how suddenly I've begun to describe women in terms of their attractiveness to men? I was utterly appalled by myself.

"Hi, you guys!" she said in an outrageous drawling American accent, "I'm Gerry from Texas. This here is my first time in England, and I'm gonna get my Certificate to show my Pop what I'm made of."

We all laughed at her accent, like something off the television. She was tall with long brown hair all plaited up and dressed like a cowgirl with a checked shirt and denim jeans. I stepped up next and kept it short and sweet.

"Good afternoon, I'm Jill Crewe, brought up in Oxfordshire, now living in Scotland sometimes. I've worked off and on at the local riding school and want to get a Certificate to help my career prospects working with horses."

This was pretty vague, and, of course, I didn't mention wanting to ride in the Olympics. In fact, it probably made me sound like the most boring of all the Horsemasters.

Next was a young man with big brown eyes and a crop of very curly dark hair springing away from his head.

"Guten afternoon," he began in a distinct German accent. "I am Dieter Schunker from Germany, and I do dressage. I have job in a riding Schule, and I go back to teach."

Wow! Here was a kindred spirit, I thought. I had been to Germany and done dressage! Perhaps I would be able to practise my German with him!

The next girl was tall and slender with wispy brown hair that floated around her egg-shaped head.

"Hello, I'm Willow Vetch. My godmother has sent me here as the family didn't really know what to do with me . ." There was an uneasy silence from the group, waiting for what she might say next. She shrugged slightly.

The next student stepped up to fill the uneasy silence. He was chunky, matter-of-fact, complete antithesis to the ghostly Willow.

"My name is Bob Nutley. I'm from Tavistock. My father runs a garage, but I prefer horses to cars. I want to work with horses, and this seemed a good start."

There was a collective sigh of relief. He was the epitome of 'normal', and the Blue Ride seemed like it might need some down to earth influence. All told, we were a cabinet of curiosities!

Alas, the last member of the ride was none other but a clone of Susan Pyke, or rather Susan King who was now married. She had that haughty look in her eye, and blonde hair that she tossed nonchalantly around her shoulders and arctic blue eyes that seemed to bore holes in you. Her name was strangely enough Eustacia Pitt. 'She is the Pitts' I thought to myself.

"Good afternoon all," she said as if addressing the knitting circle of the local Women's Institute. "My name is Eustacia Pitt, and I've been riding all my life. I've come down to do the course at the behest of my mother, who seems to think that I would benefit from a little tuition." It sounded like she thought she knew it all!

Colonel Whetton stepped up then.

"Now that's the students. We find that the comradeship created by being part of a team is very character building. I hope that you'll make sure that you work together as a group. Each of you will be assigned one of the school horses. That horse will be your responsibility for mucking out, feeding and all other stable care. I'll pin up the list here so you can see which horse is your own, and then we'll go down to the stables, and you will meet your assigned horse. But of course, you will be *riding* different horses all the time."

This was interesting. This was what I was here for. We crowded around to read the list:

Red Ride

Georgina Beeston - Carousel

Oswald Tettington-Ford - Wycombe

Henrietta Snook - Rosy

Angela Cartwright - Sunset

Pablo Rodriguez Camellia – Treasure

Ariel Bergman – Spirit Dancer

Blue Ride

Geraldine Royston - Banjo

Jill Crewe – Sausage Roll

Dieter Schunker - Hector

Willow Vetch - Tabitha

Bob Nutley - Dragon

Eustacia Pitt - Duke

I saw that my horse was called Sausage Roll.

"That is ridiculous!" I muttered to myself. Every other horse on the list had an elegant, or at least horse-like name, yet mine was named after a meaty savoury. I wondered if this was a joke or a misprint, but it was hard to imagine how Sausage Roll was any sort of misprint. To my fury Ariel the Nordic Beauty had a horse called Spirit Dancer! This did not bode well! If I had ever believed that the gods would mete out special punishment to those over-endowed with beauty and gifts, then I was sure that Ariel would disprove the theory.

As we walked down to the stable, I was fuming. I imagined that there was smoke pouring out of my ears. I could hear the riders behind me tittering about my horse's ridiculous name. I dreaded to think what he might actually look like!

My room-mate Gerry-the-American was chattering away.

"My horse is called Banjo, because I'm from the US of A. Like I'm a country singer from Nashville!"

"Well, Wycombe was the dashing rascal who seduced Mr Darcy's little sister Georgiana," said Oswald, no doubt trying to show off his knowledge of the classics.

"Duke is a suitably aristocratic title for a person of my calibre," gloated Eustacia, the horrible show-off.

The stable yard was brick-paved and had recently been renovated. The old-fashioned stalls had been knocked through, and there was an additional wing built, so all the horses were able to enjoy the comfort of a spacious loose box, rather than just a narrow space where they had to remain tied up all night. The horses must have heard the bunch of chattering, excited students coming towards them and their heads were all hanging over the half-doors watching the entrance of the stable yard expectantly.

"You'll find your horse as they all have nameplates on their stable doors," announced Colonel Whetton in a loud voice that he projected in a way that would ring around any parade ground. I looked down the line and could hear students crying out.

"Here's mine, ... He is perfectly lovely!"

"What a grand fellow!"

"She's the sweetest mare I've ever set eyes on!"

I didn't hold out much hope for a horse with a name like Sausage Roll. Sure enough, I was right. I located him at the end of the line.

He was a solid, plain brown cob with a thick neck and a scruffy mane. I looked over the half door to check him out. He had a straight shoulder and a long, almost swayback. I wondered how this ancient old cart horse had managed to be included in the school's horses and how I had drawn the short straw! It was a dark and evil mystery!

I could hear the other Horsemasters letting themselves into the loose boxes and oohing and aahhhing over their wonderful mounts. I could manage no more than a peremptory pat for the ignominiously name Sausage Roll. I stood there disconsolately. As Cruel Fate would have it Spirit Dancer and Ariel were in the loose box next door enjoying the beginning of a beautiful friendship. I didn't want to stare but couldn't help noticing that Spirit Dancer was a lovely silver grey, with a heart-breakingly beautiful Arab head, huge liquid eyes, neat, curved ears and a delicate muzzle that could fit into a teacup.

"When you've all finished introducing yourself to your equine partners, we'll do a quick tour of the stable yard," called out Colonel Whetton.

He led us in a ragged group around to the muck heap, the shed where the tools were kept, then a large tack room lined with saddle racks with plenty of room for us all to crowd in as tack-cleaning was sure to be high on the agenda. The feed room had a big noticeboard where the individual feeds were detailed for each horse, and mouse-proof bins storing every type of feed one could imagine.

"You will begin your stable duties from tomorrow morning. Report here at six-thirty, and then breakfast will be at eight-fifteen. That will give you time to muck out, feed, and clean the yard then back to the house to change into your best bib and tucker for breakfast. Then into the indoor school mounted by nine-thirty," announced Colonel Whetton in a very no-nonsense manner. "You're expected to appear at dinner clean and respectable, if not in evening dress, at seven-thirty." He added. "There is a timetable pinned up on the noticeboard in the hall, please make sure that you're punctual, or there will be *consequences.*"

He didn't say what the consequences might be, but his tone was implacable. I felt overwhelmed. Not only should I try and remember the names of all the members of Blue Ride at least, there were the horses' names and most important of all, the schedule. I decided I would get my notebook and copy down the timetable and imprint it on my mind.

Horsemasters' Timetable

6.30 am Stable Duties

8.15 am Breakfast (dressed for riding)

9.30 am Indoor Riding School mounted

11.30 am Morning Tea

12.00 pm Tack cleaning and grooming

1.00 pm Lunch

2.00 pm Free time

3.00 pm Lecture

5.00 pm Evening stables

7.00 pm Dinner

I went back to my room to get changed for dinner. I carefully hung up my two evening dresses. Obviously, they were not going to be needed. Unless, of course, Jack were to whisk me away to an exotic restaurant for a secret candlelit dinner. But now I had to admit that it was unlikely that my path would even cross Jack's and if it did, I would be too exhausted from the punishing schedule to manage even an enchanting smile in his direction. I wasn't sure that one could even find an exotic restaurant in this quiet corner of Exmoor.

I had to admit that dinner that night was fun. Blue Ride sat on one side of the table and Red Ride on the other. I wondered if this was to encourage the idea that we were competing with each other, although no clear competition had been defined. Perhaps that was to come. I sat between Dieter and Willow, opposite my rival for Jack's affections, Ariel. who was flanked by Oswald and Pablo. Obviously, the two male members of Red Ride were intent on paying homage to the ethereal Swedish beauty. I didn't fancy Oswald's chances in the face of Pablo's *latino* charm that exuded from every pore.

Everyone seemed excited at being here. We were chattering ten to the dozen, calling across the table and bandying jolly remarks all over the place.

"I was in Germany last February for a month, at a dressage stable near München," I said to Dieter. His solemn brown eyes lit up.

"Did you learn a lot?" he asked.

"Yes, it was wonderful. The whole dressage thing enchants me," I said, being careful to speak slowly and enunciate my words clearly. I knew what it was like to be surrounded by a foreign language. "Where do you come from?"

"I live near Frankfurt, in a small village. There is a farm there where they breed dressage horses. I hope to get a job helping to break in and train the horses."

"That sounds brill," I said, then I saw him frowning, obviously 'brill' wasn't in his vocabulary. "Brill is short for brilliant," I explained.

"That is good. You help me with my English," he said very seriously.

Then, I turned to Willow and began a conversation.

"You said that your godmother sent you here," I said. "Is she interested in horses?"

"My godmother," she said her eyes rolling wildly. "How did you know about my godmother?" As if she thought I was in the Secret Service and trying to trick her into some admission.

"When we introduced ourselves, you told us all," I said slowly as if reminding a small, backward child of their previous action.

"Did I?" she asked, verging on hysteria.

This woman was obviously a fruit loop, I thought to myself. I hoped she wasn't going to throw a fit and start hurling plates and cutlery.

"Do you ride horses a lot?" I asked, thinking that this might be simpler to veer her away from the touchy subject of her godmother.

"Yes," she replied emphatically and fixed me with an intense gaze, her eyes goggling, her egg-shaped head nodding up and down. I made a mental note to never sit anywhere near this one again. She was obviously a looney of the first order. I gazed down into my half-eaten plate of roast lamb and began to eat industriously, hoping that she would turn away and look at someone else. She was freaky.

The food here was very good, of the same quality as what had been served up to the Equitators. I thought I was going to need as much delicious nourishment as possible to keep up with the punishing schedule for the next fifteen weeks, not to mention dealing with some of the other students. Pablo called out to me from across the table.

"Jill Crewe!

"Yes!" I called back. It was as if we were shouting to each other across a field.

"Where do you live in Scotland? I have a friend who I write to who lives in Edinburgh."

I was terrifically grateful to Pablo for rescuing me from my doomed conversation with Willow, although he did seem to assume that everyone in Scotland knew everyone else in Scotland.

"My step-father has a place called Blainstock Castle in the Highlands."

"That sounds wonderfully romantic. Is it a proper castle?" asked Gerry in her drawling American accent. She was full of enthusiasm, just as we Britishers believed was typical of the Americans. All Americans loved castles, I thought, thinking of *Riders from Afar*, written by one of the Pullein-Thompson sisters.

"It sure is," I said, mimicking her accent good-naturedly. "There are dead animals hanging from the walls and Medieval weapons, ready for us to defend ourselves from marauders."

"Gee whiz, that sounds nuts!" she said.

Suddenly I was glad that she was my room-mate, if it had been Willow, I don't think I could have slept at night thinking that she might murder me in my bed.

After we had finished a most delicious and filling dessert of hot custard poured over stewed fruit, I felt much better. Then Colonel Whetton appeared at the doorway.

"I've brought you a list of the topics that will be covered in the written exam. You'll have lectures on each of these topics. Some written information will be handed out, but you'll be expected to write out your own notes. There will be various reference books that you will need to study. You'll find those books on the shelves in the library, where you can all sit and study. I would suggest an hour or two after dinner every night. Some of you will have to go and see to last night checks of the horses, top up water and make sure their rugs are straight."

We barely suppressed a collective groan. It would be very bad form to show reluctance at this point. It was what we were here for, to learn. I hoped that all my years of reading stable management books was going to stand me in good stead. I was determined to get through this course with honours if it was the last thing I did. We sat there scanning the list. I couldn't think of one possible topic that wasn't on it. We were going to have to be walking equestrian encyclopaedias to get through this!

I went to bed early and snuggled down into a comfortable nest. I had that tired feeling when your brain has been working overtime, adjusting to a new place. I could barely wait until tomorrow when I would begin being a Horsemaster. I was utterly determined to be the Best Horsemaster that Porlock Vale had ever seen.

| 11 |

Chapter Eleven – The First Week

The alarm clock rang, and it took me just two seconds to remember where I was. I leapt out of bed and into my working clothes. I shouted to Gerry to wake up, and I heard her groaning from under a mountain of blankets. I didn't wait for her. I zipped down the stairs and put my boots on at the back door. Then, ran down to the stable yard. I had expected to be there first, but a young woman was standing in the middle of the yard.

"Name?" she barked at me.

"Jill Crewe," I replied. "And yours?"

"Augusta Frobisher," she announced proudly.

That's a mouthful, I thought to myself.

"Head Girl!" she went on. "Be warned! I hate Sloth!"

That was a warning and a half!

Augusta consulted her list.

"You're Sausage Roll," she said, pointing towards his stable.

'I'm a Sausage Roll,' I thought to myself with a wry inward smile.

But I was in too good a mood to be upset by the imperious manner of Head Girl Augusta. If she was efficient, all the better.

The German boy came into the stable yard next.

"Name?" she asked.

"Dieter Schunker," he replied.

"You're Hector."

Dieter marched over to his rather beautiful piebald horse with the sweetest blue eyes. Its mane was half black and half white.

"*Guten morgen,*" I called across to Dieter.

"*Guten morgen,*" he replied. A quick smile spilled like sunshine over his face, for a moment lighting up his customary serious expression.

Mucking out was nothing new to me, and I set to with great energy. Sausage Roll might not have won a beauty contest, but he was very obliging and moved first one way, then the other to help me work my way around his loose box. He showed no sign of vices, neither biting nor kicking. I had a little mumbled conversation with him. This horse must have seen it all, an endless stream of Horsemasters passing through the stables. He had the look of a very wise old creature. I wished he could speak English and tell me all about it.

The yard was soon bustling with twelve Horsemasters and the circus ringmaster the formidable Augusta Frobisher. Wheelbarrows of muck went backwards and forwards, and then Augusta shouted out 'Feeding'. We all lined up with a bucket, and she dished out varying amounts of chaff, bran, oats and rolled barley. Then came the filling of hay nets with sweet meadow hay, where one student held the net and the other stuffed in the hay. I noticed that Ariel the Angelic Beauty was struggling. Obviously, she wasn't used to cleaning a stable. Perhaps she lived in a mansion with legions of servants, I thought cattily, forgetting for a moment that the stables at Blainstock Castle had a stable manager and a groom and various other bods who did all the work.

We dashed back to the house to wash and change and get down to breakfast, then out to tack up and ride across to the indoor school. I mounted Sausage Roll, and he stood quietly, solid as a rock. I gave him a gentle squeeze with my calves, and he walked forward quietly. This wasn't the case with some of the other horses. I observed carefully. I was going to have to ride all these horses by the end of the course. It would give me some idea of what I was in for. I was determined to prove that I wasn't just a pretty rider sitting on a superbly trained horse like Skydiver. It had taken me years to get to own a horse like Skydiver.

Georgie, the farmer-girl from Cheshire seemed to have been given the most tempestuous and scary of horses. He was innocuously called Carousel, which rather suggested a well-trained merry-go-round horse, but perhaps Devil might have been more appropriate. He was perhaps only 16 hh but he seemed enormous with huge hindquarters, a broad chest and a prominent Roman nose with wide-blown nostrils. The other horses were walking quietly, but he was plunging up and down like a warhorse about to assail the enemy. He looked as if he was preparing to throw his head down and give us all a demonstration of how the best of bucking broncos performed.

"How the hell did I get this one?" gasped Georgie, who was displaying an admirably strong seat and a determined character, trying to master this monster.

"We're all going to ride him at some point," said little Ettie of limited riding experience. "I think I will die if I have to ride him. Thank goodness I have my darling pink little Rosy."

"I wouldn't be seen dead on a pink horse, too girly for me," said Bob Nutley contemptuously.

"Surely they can't expect us to ride that Carousel, half of us will be killed," said Oswald in his perfectly correct elocution voice.

I thought to myself that the Horsemasters were going to have to prove that they were made of sterner stuff than the pampered Equitators. Porlock Vale seemed determined to turn out the very bravest and the best for their qualified instructors.

We walked around the arena and then in marched Colonel Whetton to put us through our paces. Sausage Roll was a little uninspiring, but he was very well-schooled, and he made it easy for me. Poor Georgie barely managed to walk when told to walk, then trot, and then when the order came through to canter Carousel dropped his inside shoulder and gave a fine display of three bone-shattering bucks. Georgie was certainly a stalwart character. She managed to drag his head up and drove him forward. He crow-hopped, bouncing stiff-leggedly across the arena, then he plunged his head down, and this time he twisted as he threw himself forward and Georgie could no longer stick to him. She flew through the air and landed on her rather well-upholstered bottom.

Bob Nuttley made the mistake of laughing when she fell off.

Carousel was foaming from the mouth like a rabid dog.

"Mr Nuttley, let us see how you can handle this horse," said Colonel Whetton who had got hold of Carousel's reins. "Miss Beeston if you are not hurt, you can ride Mr Nuttley's Dragon."

Dragon was a very plain, bay horse, as stolid and unimaginative as Bob Nuttley. The ride continued to walk on while we watched agog as Bob strode towards the centre of the arena. Colonel Whetton held Carousel while he mounted. We all gasped in astonishment. Carousel walked on quietly like a little mouse as if butter wouldn't melt.

"What is that all about?" muttered Georgie who looked disappointed, riding around on Dragon.

"Life is sometimes stranger than fiction," announced Angela, obviously a master of the cliché.

When we had finished walking, trotting and cantering, we changed rein and rode without stirrups. Our positions were corrected mercilessly and then we had to practise sitting trot. Sausage Roll was certainly sweet-natured and obedient, but with his straight shoulder and up-and-down carthorse movement, he was extremely uncomfortable at the sitting trot. By the time we dismounted, my legs felt like chewed string.

Morning tea was served at the long table in the tack room, so we didn't have to waste time dashing up to the house. We tucked into big doorstep slices of bread and butter with a choice of jams and marmalade, and also some sliced cheese and tomato and huge mugs of tea. We were all starving and even the ethereal Ariel, who looked like a dream fairy and not subject to mortal appetites, was munching on a thick slice heaped with cheese and tomato.

One of the kitchen staff came in and cleared away the plates and mugs, and we settled down to clean the tack. We were left alone and began discussing our experiences of the morning.

"My horse is the most bad-tempered brute I've ever encountered. Talk about a chestnut mare with white-rimmed eyes. She just takes the cake," said Angela.

"She nearly kicked the eye out of sweet Rosy who I'm sure has never harmed a fly in her life," replied Etta.

"Carousel!" said Georgie.

"What is going on with that horse, one minute a bucking bronco and then as quiet as pie," I contributed.

"He probably recognised a decent rider," said Bob Nuttley in such a smug, self-satisfied way that three people threw wet sopping sponges at him. He promptly chucked them back.

"Well, Banjo might sound like an American instrument, but I can't get a tune out of him, and he sure doesn't know how to neck rein," said Gerry.

"No-one neck reins in England, we ride properly here," said Oswald in his maddeningly posh voice.

"Oh, lah-dee-dah!" mocked Gerry, who seemed unfailingly cheerful and absolutely refused to take offence at any remarks thrown at her.

"I like my Hector very much," said Dieter, perhaps trying to be more positive.

"Yes, and Spirit Dancer, he is divine," breathed Ariel.

We were finishing our tack when Augusta came in and inspected such things as beneath the buckles, tested the stitching on the stirrup leathers and made sure every bit was sparkling. Then she ordered us out to groom the horses.

After lunch, we had an hour's free time, except for Willow, Bob, Angela and Oswald who were sent down to the Equitators' stable to clean some tack and groom and get the horses ready for the Equitators' afternoon session. I felt like collapsing in a heap, but pushed myself on and went with Pablo, Dieter and Etta down to the village to walk along the beach. Dieter and I talked in a mixture of German and English, and

Pablo and Etta ran around like children, skipping into the waves with their shoes off. The water was icy cold. The village houses were huddled together as if to ward off the storms that must flow in from the ocean. I wondered again what it might be like to live by the sea.

We got back to the big house in time for our lecture from Miss Follett. We had pens and pencils, notes and exercise books. A blackboard stood at the front of the room, and Miss Follett was writing up headings.

"We will begin with you telling me everything you know about stable management," she said. "And then we will fill in the gaps."

I was struck by what a wonderful teacher she was. If only all my school teachers could have been this practical and thorough, I might have flown through my school exams with some A grades.

By the time I fell into bed that night, I didn't have a moment to think back over my day. I was asleep in seconds, utterly exhausted.

The next morning my first thought was, which horse do I get to ride today. Please, please God not Carousel! In fact, I don't think any of us would have minded if Carousel had died in the night, but he was alive and well. It was impossible to tell what type of mood he was in as he eyed us up over his stable door as we stumbled across the yard. He was enigmatic, and that made him all the more dangerous. When he was good, he was very, very good and when he was bad, he was murderous.

We didn't find out which horse we were assigned until after breakfast when we crowded around the list on the noticeboard. Today I was given Rosy, the sweetest pink pony mare in the world. Etta had been given Sausage Roll, and I did rather wonder whether I was being put into the 'beginner' category like her. But anything was better than bones broken by the Crazy Carousel, to be ridden by Eustacia today. She and Bob Nuttley had ganged up to become the Terrible Twosome and seemed to enjoy having a go at the rest of us, especially those who weren't able to defend themselves.

We had another arduous session with Colonel Whetton, who was in the Mrs Darcy category of teaching. Although not old-fashioned in terms of the backward seat that was still lingering around in the dark corners of Medieval Britain, he did believe in mastering the basics. I was looking forward to the dressage lesson tomorrow with Captain Romanski.

Rosy was so easy to ride, she was positively uninspiring. But I tried my very hardest to get the best out of her. I was waiting eagerly for Carousel to throw the toffy-nosed Eustacia on her elegant behind, but he behaved in an exemplary fashion, possibly saving up all his bad behaviour for the hapless rider to whom he would be assigned tomorrow.

That afternoon I was one of the four to go and wait on the Equitators. I was secretly thrilled, thinking that this would be my chance to see Jack again. Once he realised I was here, I hoped that he might make an effort to spend some time with me. I walked down to the other stable yard with Pablo, Dieter and Ariel. I was the only Britisher amongst them. If only it had not been Ariel chosen this afternoon. If Jack were there, her beauty would far eclipse any good looks I might possess.

It was strange. I had never really thought about whether or not I was good-looking. I knew that I was not pig-ugly and that on occasion, I could scrub up reasonably well, but I had never really dwelled upon the idea of being pretty or not. When I was younger, I had carefully applied lipstick and face powder, but it was only to make me look older, not to enhance any beauty I might have. No matter how nice-looking I was, I could not hold a candle to Ariel, with her sweet, breathy voice and fluttering eyelashes.

I knew that my eyes were an attractive bright blue and not too small. My nose tip-tilted, which Mummy had once told me, was very photogenic. My mouth was reasonable, my lips neither thick nor thin and perhaps the overall effect was pleasant. Mummy did not go so far as to tell me that a man would have to love me for my pilgrim soul, which was what Joanna Cannan was reputed to have said to her eldest daughter Josephine Pullein-Thompson. But, nor did Mummy tell me that I would stun the world with my beauty. I had always believed that character was important and that one would be admired for inner strength and also perhaps for being witty and lively. I would have to be as witty as I could be, if I were to shine next to Ariel who might be beautiful but whose grasp of English was rudimentary, making her a less than entertaining conversationalist.

We arrived at the other stables and set to work polishing the saddles and bridles and then working on the horses. For all my prognostications over how Jack might see me, he was nowhere in sight. This bunch of Equitators were more or less beginners and riding the school's second string of horses who were well-trained, quiet and not at all problematic compared to the motley lot of steeds designated to the Horsemasters. I guessed that rank beginners held no charm for Jack, so he left it to the others. This afternoon Augusta Frobisher was teaching, and I watched with interest. Her teaching style was, like her stable management style, extremely efficient if rather uninspiring.

We didn't have to wait until the end of the lesson as we needed to be back for our three o'clock lecture on stable management. We marched back down the lane. Pablo was oozing charm all over Ariel who smiled at him quietly, accepting such adoration as her due.

I slept dreamlessly that night and woke the next morning feeling excited that today would be Captain Romanski's dressage lesson. I tucked into a hearty breakfast and went to check the list. I couldn't believe it. I had been allocated Carousel! The horse that would behave for several days before he had another brainstorm. It was dangerously close to the time for him to have another bucking fit and I had drawn the short straw. Augusta had told us yesterday that they kept Carousel so that we might learn to sit a bucking horse as most of us rarely had that sort of experience. She said that at the Spanish Riding School they used the horses that performed the capriole, that leap into the air with the kicking out of hind legs, specifically to teach riders to sit a buck. I wished that they employed that practice here instead of a devil horse of uncertain temperament.

I tried to stay calm and not betray my nervousness. A horse immediately senses fear, and I suspected that with such a strange temperament Carousel would snuff up the mood of his rider with accurate perception. I mounted carefully and Dieter, stepped forward to hold

Carousel's head until I was settled in the saddle. Dieter was such a gentleman!

I felt a quiver run through Carousel's body, and I knew that it was going to be one of his bucking days. I had thought about how one rode a bucking horse and concluded that in the first place, it was paramount to prevent the horse getting his head down between his knees. But once he succeeded, the best manoeuvre was to lean back and swing one's legs forwards and then back again as he landed. Certainly, I had never been taught how to sit a bucking horse at Mrs Darcy's riding school!

As we rode up the lane, Dieter came up beside me. He was mounted on Sausage Roll, and he used him to push up beside Carousel, in an effort to force him into some sort of submission. Carousel walked as if on hot coals, tip-tupping. I knew that once the lesson started his fury would be unleashed.

We walked around the arena, and Captain Romanski entered quietly. Although elderly, he was lean and elegant, and his composure was tangible. He would be a cavalry officer until the day he died. I thought how strange it was that my first dressage lesson as a Horsemaster would undoubtedly be a lesson in sitting a bucking horse. Or at least a chance to practise a type of rolling fall used by jockeys to prevent a broken neck.

Captain Romanski ordered each of us to lengthen our stirrups by two holes. This was a slightly different position to that advocated by Colonel Whetton. I wanted to beg him to allow me to stay the way I was. It would be harder to sit a bucking horse with longer stirrups.

Carousel walked and trotted, but I felt him broiling inside, and when the order came to canter, he began to plunge up and down. I had observed his routine the other day, and I knew that this was the prelude to a bucking frenzy. I shortened my reins so he could not reef them through my fingers and get his head between his knees. I waited, and then he dropped his shoulder, which was the sly trick of a horse who knew how to rid himself of a rider. I leaned the other way and kept a tight grip on the reins. He leapt into the air, like an antelope and tried to reef his head down as he plunged forward. I remembered to lean back, but now it was simply a matter of seeing how many bucks I could sit before I was thrown. I wrapped my lower leg around the girth, and tried to swing in time with Carousel's movement. I felt his fury writhing beneath me. Something drove this horse to fight so hard. I sat him out for six more bucks and then I couldn't cope any more, and I was flying through the air, I tried to remember to tuck my head in. I felt the impact of my body hitting the sand, and I lay there for just a moment but then managed to stagger to my feet.

If, I were to follow the tenets of all horsemen than I should mount again. There was silence. No-one dared laugh this time, or it would be them remounting.

"Do you wish to get back on?" asked Captain Romanski. I vaguely wondered how he managed to be so courteous.

I dithered. Had Carousel done his worst? Now it was out of his system would he proceed to behave in his 'reasonable mode'. I decided that I would. I hated the idea of failing. I nodded grimly, and Captain Romanski held him while I mounted. I sat there, waiting. Would he explode or walk on quietly? I could feel his indecision.

"Come on you, horrible horse," I said firmly, feeling much braver than I had when I had first mounted this morning. He walked on quietly. The Horsemasters cheered me. I felt like a conquering hero. The rest of the lesson passed peacefully, and surprisingly Carousel was good to ride when he wasn't going mental.

Captain Romanski explained about different ways of teaching beginners the rudiments of dressage. This was new to me, but it was obvious that the main aim of our course was to become Instructors. Up until now, I'd just gone my own sweet merry way delivering lessons but now I realised, and this is probably totally obvious to most of you, that there is an art to teaching that can be learned and mastered.

When the lesson was over, I felt hugely relieved. I had so dreaded riding Carousel, and now I had done it. I wasn't sure if I'd learned how to sit a bucking horse, but I certainly had more of an idea than previously. I looked forward to riding all the other horses now. It was like going to a restaurant and sampling everything on the menu.

We rode back up to the stable yard, and Dieter smiled at me shyly.
"You did well," he said.

After lunch, some of the others were going to the beach, but I decided to sit in the library and look at some magazines. I had to get over
the excitement of the morning. I leafed through *Année Hippique,* and,
inevitably my mind drifted back to Jack. No-one had mentioned him,
and I hadn't seen him. Perhaps he was away again. I decided that I must
make an effort to find out where he was. I would go down to the other
stable yard, and perhaps I could find Ruth and casually bring up the
subject. I hated to be this desperate female in pursuit of a man, but
everything at Porlock Vale reminded me of him. If I were to be enrap-
tured with a man, then I may as well play the part of an infatuated female.

| 12 |

Chapter Twelve – Assorted Horses

The days whizzed by at the speed of light. On Saturday morning was our hack through the countryside led by Augusta. The day was sunny, one of those beautiful autumn sunny days when there is a hint of nostalgia and sadness at the passing of another summer. I sound like I've lived through fifty summers with not many more to go with that last sentence!

The bright sunlight lit up the landscape, and we were taken along a track from where we could see the creamy edge of the waves rippling along the stoney beach below us. On our right were steeply wooded hills that rose up above the road and we knew that beyond was the moorland. A light breeze played across the hills, dancing up the slopes and down into the deep valleys lined with ferns that were beginning to brown. The horses' hoofs clopped, and a crow cawed plaintively from a nearby tree. We rode our own horses for the hacks, and I was on Sausage Roll, who I was beginning to love. He had such a faithful, good temperament that I no longer scorned him for his slightly too-long back and straight shoulder. At least he was honest. Poor Georgie was on the wicked Carousel who was rolling his eyes and tossing his head, his hoofs lifting high in the air. The other Horsemasters rode their

JILL AND THE HORSEMASTERS — 147

horses in a crowd around him to try to stem the flow of his ill-temper. Except Angela on Sunset, she had to keep to the back on her mean-spirited chestnut mare, who kicked like hell with her squinty eyes and permanently laid-back ears. Bob and Eustacia rode out in front whispering between themselves, no doubt plotting some nasty piece of bullying.

We came to the moorland and set off in single file along a rough track with brown furze and ferns along the edges. I lifted my face to the sky and enjoyed the feeling of open air. We seemed to have been trotting around the dusty indoor arena forever. It was good to be out in the open. I let the wind blow through my brain.

Soon we came to a long gentle slope where the track widened and two abreast, we cantered, perching lightly over our horses' shoulders, as if we were race-riders doing morning exercise. I found myself cantering next to Willow, who rode a funny old horse called Tabitha. She was a scrawny, flea-bitten grey mare, full of fads and crotchets, and although she didn't burst into bucking frenzies like Carousel, nor kick the eye out of a needle like Sunset-the-Red-Witch, she continually shook her head as if she had a bee in her ears. I noticed that she dished widely with her front feet, which didn't move forward in a straight line, but rather in a curve that looked horribly ungainly.

"What is Tabitha like to ride?" I asked, feeling the need to make polite conversation.

Willow shrugged. She was a hopeless conversationalist, but I didn't give up.

"Are you enjoying it here?" I asked. I know that this was the blandest of all questions, but I couldn't think of anything original or interesting and Weird Willow was a bit freaky. It wasn't just her wispy hair and egg-shaped head but her goggling eyes. She fixed me in an intense gaze.

"Are you in love?"

Normally, I would have thought that she was merely projecting towards me her own preoccupation, but with my secret obsession with Jack Laskey I was vulnerable. How had I betrayed my feelings and dreams? Did Willow have strange psychic powers?

"I don't think so," I replied uncertainly, then threw it back at her.

"Are you?" I asked.

"Yes," she hissed. "But they sent me away as they said he was no good. He is after my money."

"Oh," I replied. "That sounds like something out of a romantic novel. You've got fifteen weeks of intensive riding and stable work, and then you're meant to forget all about him."

She began to laugh, the strange high-pitched laughter of a looney, like Mr Rochester's mad wife locked in the attic. I decided that further conversation might be dangerous, but I was rather fascinated. Willow didn't look like an heiress who might be targeted by fortune-hunters, but I really didn't know what such an heiress might look like.

"Where do you live?" I asked, thinking this might lead to safer ground and perhaps yield more information.

"Mostly in London, at my father's house, but he's not there he's usually in America."

I was intrigued now and decided to go for broke.

"How much money do you have?" I asked.

She shrugged.

"I don't know, I've never counted it. I'm an only child. My mother died when I was born, and my godmother takes an interest in me. They don't actually let me have the money, but I know it's there."

I looked at her carefully. She could ride but not in any spectacular or impressive way. Obviously, horses weren't her first passion. What a strange young woman. I couldn't imagine a man falling in love with her in the ordinary course of events. She seemed to be either deeply withdrawn or teetering on the edge of hysteria.

We had ridden to the top of a hill, high above the moorland. We stopped to look at the view. Augusta gestured back towards the sea.

"This is the best view, of the sea, and in this direction," she swung her arm the other way, "is the moorland. On the way back we might see some Exmoor ponies, one of the herds likes to camp in the valley through the winter."

"Wild ponies!" exclaimed Etta, in a high-pitched, childish voice.

"They're not that wild," said Augusta, as usually correcting everyone. "They're brought in regularly by the farmers who own them. They worm them and take the foals off them so that the mares don't end up with three foals still suckling. Often, they send the foals to the sales, some of them keep them and break them in and sell them on as riding ponies. One of our ex-students works as a pony breaker, for Titch McRory who lives over that way. He owns a lot of this herd."

"I would love a job like that," said Etta. "Imagine it, every day training the sweet ponies."

"They're probably not that sweet when they're trying to buck you off," said Bob a little contemptuously. I vaguely wished that Carousel had bucked Bob off the other day. Perhaps next time it was his turn.

We got back for lunch, and Blue Ride disappeared off on a jaunt, piling into Angela's old Land Rover.

But I didn't mind a quiet weekend of just stable work, and then Augusta turned up and announced that we should spring clean the tack room. There was a quiet groan from all of us, but we didn't argue.

"Ours is not to question why," I quoted bravely, trying to jolly everyone along.

In the evening, I went up to my room intent on some quiet study, sitting up in bed with my week's notes, but I fell asleep within minutes. The punishing schedule of activities was wearing me out. I didn't even hear Gerry come stumbling in after an expedition to the local pub with some of the working pupils.

On Monday morning, I saw that I was assigned Spirit Dancer, the beautiful silver-grey Arab looked after by Ariel, who had unfortunately drawn the short straw and had been given Carousel. We got down to the riding arena and who should stride in, not Colonel Whetton but Jack Laskey. My heart began to hammer inside my chest. How fortuitous that I should be riding the most elegant and beautiful of horses on the day that Jack and I were destined to meet again.

He didn't look at all surprised to see me.

"I'd heard you had come back as a Horsemaster, Jill," he said. "Where have you left that wonderful Skydancer?"

I thought he only cares about my horse, not me.

"I took him up to Blainstock Castle," I replied.

"You don't really live in a castle, do you?" jeered Eustacia, laughing unpleasantly.

It was beneath my dignity to reply. She was a clone of Susan Pyke!

Jack decided that we should do some jumping today and he had had some of the working pupils bring out the wings and poles. They set up three jumps, each two strides apart, a good three feet high. We were to canter around, and as we approached the first jump, we had to drop our knotted reins and cross our arms in front of our chest. I feared a little for Etta who was such a raw beginner, but she was back on Rosy who would look after her. This was going to be fun. I felt all zingy and excited to have Jack there. I wanted him to see me floating over the jumps as if I were an angel on horseback. This week was going to be wonderful, now that Jack had made an effort to come over and see me everything would go from there!

I watched carefully as Ariel jumped, and Jack showed no sign of swooning in adoration at her Nordic beauty. I hoped this meant that he preferred English girls. It never even occurred to me that he might be interested in Weird Willow, but I did notice that she came in for some quite complimentary remarks on her riding which was at best decidedly uninspiring. He was probably just being kind and trying to encourage her.

Jack followed us in for morning tea, and he was deep in conversation with Dieter about some dressage competition that he had been attending in Germany. So that was why there had been no sign of him! I heard him speaking in German to Dieter, and my heart swelled with admiration. He was no stuffy old Britisher who looked down on foreigners. He was a man of the world, an international personage!

I was so full of pretensions and dreams about Jack that I interpreted everything he did, in terms of his desire to talk to me but not to make it too obvious, in case of upsetting the applecart with him an instructor and me, a student. After morning tea, we set to our usual tack cleaning routine. He must have slipped away then, but I didn't see him go. I was bent over my saddle, polishing it within an inch of its life.

That afternoon I was on the roster to go down to the Equitators for my stint of waiting on them. I believed that this had all been designed by Fate, or perhaps even orchestrated by Jack, so that we would have time to be together. This week it was not raw beginners but a bunch of tough professional show jumpers who had arrived in a merry band to hone their skills after a hard summer of jumping around the circuit. They had all brought young horses that were to be trained through the winter. Everything was a lark, to this hardened bunch, with wise-cracks and badinage crackling through the air. I found it exhilarating and spent my time dashing into the ring and re-erecting the jumps, along with Willow, Bob and Eustacia.

Jack was instructing, and he pressed them hard. No-one seemed to think that young horses needed to be brought on slowly. It was an at-mosphere of, 'just do it!'. I carefully suppressed any of my old ideas of 'good horsemanship'. If Jack advocated this wild careless brand of equestrianism then it must be alright. Looking back, how one is blinded with love! I would never have thought that I could sink to such depths.

The showjumpers were a hard-bitten lot, and their competitiveness couldn't just be switched off. Everything was a competition. The young horses snorted and propped, rolled their eyes and arrived at the jumps, as often as not, on the wrong stride. But they were forced on, and there seemed a deliberate policy to put them wrong sometimes, to hit the jumps and 'teach them a lesson'. I didn't like this at all. I shuddered at the thought of doing this to Skydiver's delicate legs that were so good at dancing. I knew he could jump now. But the thought of forcing him over a jump on the wrong stride so that he hit it was utterly anathema to me. I was glad when we had to hurry back up the lane for our after-noon session.

Willow fell into step beside me as Eustacia and Bob hurried in front of us, whispering and hissing to each other.

"Jill, you know I did tell you that my godmother made me come here, to get me away from my boyfriend. Can I trust you with a huge secret?"

I looked at her head, which was nodding up and down like one of those dogs in the back window of a car. The last thing I wanted was to be drawn into Weird Willow's Wonderful World. It was my fault for talking to her previously. She now saw me as some sort of confidante.

"It's my boyfriend. You know, I told you, the one that they say is unsuitable. He's coming to see me."

"What here?" I asked, thinking that this was the last thing I wanted to be involved in.

"I told him I was coming here and he wrote to me this morning. You know they don't monitor our mail. My godmother didn't think of that!" she said, her voice shrill and high-pitched with excitement.

"I don't suppose they would, I mean it's not like we're in prison, or even boarding school," I said, adopting a reasonable tone.

"He's going to meet me down at the village pub tonight. Will you come with me? I don't want to walk down there by myself."

I didn't see how I could get out of it. Just for one moment of madness, I thought of inviting Jack in a sort of 'double date', but I knew that I would never be game. I also didn't think that being a friend of Willow would be much of a recommendation. She was far too weird!

"Why don't we invite some of the other Horsemasters to come with us?" I suggested, thinking there might be safety in numbers.

"If you like," she said shrugging, "but we won't tell them the secret plan."

"No, of course not," I reassured her. The less I had to do with Willow, the better, and I hardly wanted to show myself up as her 'secret confidante'. There was something very creepy about her!

I proposed the plan at the evening meal. There was a general chorus of excitement, but some of them cried off, claiming extreme fatigue. We went in a group and helped those who were in charge of the last check of the stables, when the water buckets were topped up, and each horse was looked over and rugs checked before night time.

There was a bunch of us trooping down the road to the little village; Willow, Dieter, Pablo, Ariel and Angela. Willow was in a particularly hectic mood, overly dramatic and highly strung – her wispy hair was flying around in the breeze that was coming in off the sea, her eyes shining and protruding. Vaguely I pondered on what this secret boyfriend would be like, but I guessed I would find out soon enough. Or perhaps he wouldn't turn up. Then poor Willow would be inconsolable.

The village pub was dark and cosy. There was a cheerful fire in the grate, and the ceiling was very low, painted a dark crimson colour. Pablo offered to buy a round of drinks, and Ariel went over to the bar to help him carry them over. We managed to bag a table near the fire and sat down. Willow was standing up searching the room in the most conspicuous manner possible. Evidently, the boyfriend wasn't there as she slumped down next to me with a whining sigh.

"Don't worry," I muttered. "There's plenty of time for him to turn up."

Angela was telling a funny story about her husband and his struggles with her three boisterous children. We were all laughing, except of course Willow, who was utterly obsessed with her own thoughts.

Pablo and Ariel came over with two small trays of drinks, and we began to sip. I had only ordered an orange juice. I had discovered in the past that wine bought in a pub was the very cheapest and nastiest and I couldn't quite face beer or cider, let alone spirits.

There were quite a few locals seated at the bar, but no-one seemed interested in us. I supposed they were used to the Porlock Vale students hanging around. Suddenly Willow leapt up beside me. She was on her feet and sliding across to the doorway where stood a rather handsome, tall, dark man. She really had no sense of discretion! I was rather hoping she would bring him over and introduce him, but she didn't have that sort of social grace. I watched her as she grabbed him by the arm and drew him over to a dark corner, away from the warmth of the fire.

"What on earth is she up to?" asked Angela, who was all jolly and good fun, but also rather sharp-eyed.

"She is talking to a young man," said Ariel, who might be divine looking but was very matter of fact with no talent for witty repartee or facetious humour.

"He's a looker," said Angela and I wondered if she was going to put on her glasses to inspect him more carefully.

Pablo glanced over and gave a *latino* shrug and turned back to charming Ariel.

"Are you missing your horses Jill?" Dieter asked, his lovely brown eyes kind and considerate.

"Well I could certainly do with having either of them for lessons, they're a lot easier to ride than these school horses," I said. "But really, we don't have much time for private longings. It's all just one rush from lessons, to stable, to studying theory."

"I think I will begin to spend one or two hours every night studying my notes. The exam will require a great deal of learning. Would you like to join me in this activity?" he asked.

"Yes, yes, I would," thinking what a considerate and conscientious man he was. He reminded me of the other German people I had met.

"Jill, Jill, come with me, we're going to get to meet this mystery man," said Angela, grabbing me by the arm and dragging me across the pub.

"Willow! Willow! Do introduce us," she said in a loud voice.

The young man looked up, somewhat startled. He probably hadn't realised he had an audience. He was definitely good looking, with rather strange pale skin with a sprinkling of pale freckles across his straight nose, curly dark hair and blue eyes.

"This is Reg," said Willow, ungracious and awkward.

"Hello, I'm Angela. How do you do?" Angela thrust her hand towards him in a mandatory handshake.

"I'm Jill, good to meet you," I muttered out of the corner of my mouth, looking longingly back at the group of Horsemasters.

"So, Reg," said Angela, lingering over his name, which was a little ordinary. "Do tell, how do you know Willow?"

Reg flushed bright red and obviously didn't want to tell.

"We're busy," said Willow. "Do you mind?"

Angela was forced to back down, and I dragged her off.

"That was embarrassing," I bleated.

"But she must know him from somewhere else," said Angela her rather long nose quivering with curiosity.

"Who cares," I shrugged.

When it was time to leave Willow had disappeared. Perhaps they were out the back canoodling or sitting in his car planning an elopement to Gretna Green. I felt no compunction in hightailing it back to Porlock Vale without her.

She turned up at breakfast, looking unusually composed, her hair pulled back in a neat bun and her eyes downcast as she ate her way through a large bowl of creamy porridge.

"Was it fun seeing your young man, last night?" I asked as we walked down to the stables for our riding lesson.

"Yes, he was telling me about his family. You know he is in exile, from a small Eastern European country, but he can't talk about it," she explained. But she was curiously calm, not her usual melodramatic, uptight self.

"Gosh, that is rather exotic," I said, not believing a word of it.

That morning I was thrilled to be designated Treasure, which was the horse that Pablo looked after. He was a beautiful bay gelding, perfectly formed with long, slender legs, an elegant neck, a noble head and very alert, intelligent ears. I mounted eagerly and was delighted with his long, light stride and his soft mouth and correct head carriage. I believed that as far as the school's horses went, he was the pick of the bunch.

I noticed that Eustacia was riding Sausage Roll and her outside leg constantly niggled at him, jabbing him in the ribs. Whenever Colonel Whetton wasn't looking, she jerked cruelly at his mouth. I was outraged but knew that if I said anything at all, she would be all the worse and take it out on the poor honest horse. She was worse than Susan Pyke, who was basically just a hopeless rider. Eustacia was deliberately cruel – she knew exactly what she was doing! I would have to make a fuss of Sausage Roll this afternoon and perhaps take him out to graze at the grass verges. That was one thing about Porlock Vale that I found annoying, the horses had no turnout at all. They never got to wander around a field, drop their heads and nose around the grass and snuff the wind as it blew through their manes. I wondered if I might say something to Jack and see if he could change the routine.

Today we were jumping, and it was a positive joy to ride Treasure flying over any combination that we were set. He had a delicate stride that could be shortened or lengthened with the lightest of aids. Colonel Whetton was teaching us how to turn the horse at a diagonal in the midst of combination fences where the striding was awkward, or to rescue ourselves if we'd come in wrong. This was highly technical, and although I might have done it by chance in the past, I'd never ridden so strategically before. I was nursing my secret plan to start jumping Skydiver, and I knew that he would be a master at such techniques with his advanced dressage training.

I admired Etta mounted on Rosy. This was far beyond beginner standard, and she was proving herself up to it. It couldn't be easy for someone who had only recently never jumped anything over two feet six! My brave American roommate Gerry was riding Carousel, but fortunately, he was in a good mood today and not determined to unseat his poor hapless rider. He was an impressive looking horse and could certainly jump when he set his mind to it. Angela was on Spirit Dancer. I'm afraid to say that I wrote her off as a middle-aged housewife, but she could definitely ride. She wasn't stylish or elegant but more workmanlike, with a secure seat and lots of confidence. Spirit Dancer could certainly give Treasure a run for his money if it came to a jumping competition. Dieter was on Banjo, Gerry's charge, and he was getting the best out of the rather plain and lightweight old horse that had obviously seen better days. I hadn't really noticed before, but Dieter was an exceptionally good rider, but so modest and unassuming that it looked like he was sitting there, giving no aids at all, which is, of course, the mark of a brilliant rider, who looks like they're not doing anything.

Dieter and I were due to begin our study sessions tonight, meeting up in the library and comparing notes, to make sure neither of us had missed any vital pieces of information. Then we would begin to test each other on the various topics. I remembered when Ann and I had done this as teenagers, but then there had been no crucial exam at the end of it. Dieter had suggested that we start with the points of the horse which I was pretty sure I knew, but then there was a vast array of splints, curbs, ringbone and spavins and I would get hopelessly mixed up with them. I'd been fortunate enough never to have a horse with any of these ghastly growths.

The next morning was dressage day, and I was stepping across the stable yard like a cat on a hot tin roof, thinking that Jack might be teaching today. I was assigned to Hector, Dieter's horse with the crazy geometric black and white colouring and the strange blue eyes. I wished it could have been Treasure who I had ridden the day before as he made any rider worth their salt look elegant and masterful. Hector was a strange horse with some very odd quirks and to have him for a dressage lesson was rather drawing the short straw.

I rode into the arena, adjusting myself to his short, ambling stride, thinking that I must look like I was riding a clown horse. In strutted the elegant Captain Romanski and not a sign of Jack. I sighed but turned my mind to learning as much as possible. The whole lesson was an utter eye-opener, and I found that I had to unlearn a lot of what I thought was standard common-sense horse lore. It was the lesson on the halt.

"Now, what do you do when you want the horse to stop or slow down?" asked the Captain. "Eustacia?"

She gave him a smug smile, she had Treasure today and was no doubt feeling confident that she was going to shine.

"Sit down in the saddle, lean back slightly, weight in the stirrups and take a firm hold on the rein," she recited. I admit that I might have answered in the same way but with perhaps a little more emphasis on 'setting the hands' and riding into a halt.

"No! No! No!" he cried, wringing his hands in despair, and I saw Angela and Oswald suppressing their giggles.

"That is all wrong! Has anyone got a better answer?"

I considered offering up my version but decided I didn't want to put my head above the parapet and get it shot off, just in case there was a way of halting that was entirely correct and unknown to me.

Dieter was braver than me and put his hand up.

"Yes, Dieter," said Captain Romanski, and I could tell that he approved of the German student.

"You must ride into the halt so that the horse brings its legs under his body," said Dieter, quietly.

"Correct – to a point," said our instructor.

"Stay vertical, no leaning back, no pressing in your feet, no pushing out your chest. Stop your seat bones and bear down, while releasing your breath, your reins should be short enough that your horse can feel it when you press your thumbs down."

There was a murmur run around the group. Everyone was adjusting their position at the walk, getting ready for the order to halt.

"Try not to go side to side with your seat bones, the teeter-totter is what happens when you ride a cob, and we have a number of cobs here. Try not to move back and forward continuously. The horse will either run away from under you, or they will tune out, they will not listen to this horrible disconnected feeling on their backs."

Certainly, Hector was very cobby, I tried not to teeter-totter, but there were so many instructions I was finding it hard to obey them all together. I shortened my reins and checked that my thumbs were on top. I tried to keep my seat bones still, no swaying back and forward like I was rowing a boat. Then I had to think about my breathing, in and out. When the order came to halt, I made sure I gave the aid on my breathing out. Hector did halt, but he was good at downward transitions. It was the 'go faster' changes of pace that he struggled with. He was essentially very quiet, almost lazy. The whole ride came to a halt, some quicker than others.

"Now walk on, and we will begin again."

In the back of my mind, I was wondering whether this style of halting might have helped at all when Black Comedy, the ex-steeplechaser that I had bought a while ago, had taken off and jumped the hedge into the neighbouring field. He had had a mouth of concrete. Then there was the time when Skydiver had bolted when he was afraid of the thunderstorm. Perhaps these aids were more suitable when riding under very controlled conditions.

We spent half the lesson going from walk to halt and walk again.

"The take home message is breathe out for slowing down and breathe in for going faster. That is enough for now," said Captain Romanski. "We must think of the horses. I want you to canter on from the walk and give them a little alteration in the routine. Breathe in as you give the aid to canter."

Gratefully we all cantered on. Hector did a lovely transition from walk to canter, so even he the laziest horse in the bunch was pleased to go a little faster. When we were all cantering twice around the arena, Captain Romanski asked us to halt again. I had to try and remember everything we had practised at the walk. We came to various straggling halts. Pablo had been smiling at Ariel and not paying attention, and he didn't give the aid in time, and poor Sausage Roll cannoned into the back of Sunset, the nasty kicking chestnut mare, today being ridden by Oswald. She lashed out and caught him on the shoulder.

"Oh, no!" I cried, nearly jumping off to run to him.

"Wait," said the Captain. He strode over to Sausage Roll and looked him over. "Ride on Oswald. He is not lame, but perhaps later, when he cools down, he will be sore. Jill, you will attend to this horse later and tell Augusta what has happened.

We rode back to the stables.

"What happens if one of the horses becomes unsound?" asked Etta.

"They'll bring up an extra horse from the other stable," said Angela, who always liked to know everything. I wondered just how hard she was studying privately to make sure she came top in the theory exam. I felt my competitive instincts being aroused.

I fussed around Sausage Roll for ages when we got back, casting dark looks across the stable yard to that mean horrible mare, Sunset and I wasn't too pleased with Pablo for his inattention. I even gave Ariel a passing black thought as it was her beauty that had distracted the Spanish boy. Dear old Sausage Roll seemed happy enough, and I would wait until after lunch to lead him out and see if he had stiffened up. Augusta gave me some linament to rub on him. After all this morning's concentrated lesson on our halting aids, I felt like I needed some too on my poor seatbones. Now I had discovered their existence they were going to become a focal point!

| 13 |

Chapter Thirteen – Willow Disappears

I spent the spare hour after lunch leading Sausage Roll up and down the lane so he could pick at the green grass. He didn't seem lame. I was dreaming about doing perfect halts on Skydiver and Balius. It would be weeks and weeks before I would get back to training them and practising all my new knowledge and skills. I still had that secret dream of bursting in on the eventing scene with Skydiver. That would be one in the eye for Malevolent Mark!

Willow hurried past me on her way down to the village, and I gave her a distracted wave. I wouldn't have even thought twice about this, but for the events that followed. For that afternoon, she wasn't at the theory session with Miss Follett, which wasn't particularly noteworthy. We all assumed she had skived off or was nursing a sick headache in her room. But she wasn't at dinner either, and Augusta frowned and hurried off to consult with Colonel Whetton.

They asked us if we had seen her and I volunteered the information that she had walked past me toward the village soon after two o'clock this afternoon. It seemed that no-one else had seen her since then. Now if she had been murdered and I was the last person who had seen her, then I would be the prime suspect. But, I couldn't imagine that anyone would even bother to murder Willow, hardly a significant person. Or so I thought at that time!

The next morning, I think we all thought that Willow would materialise at the breakfast table, if not in the stable yard for mucking out. Dieter and I volunteered to do Tabitha, who was a mean-spirited, catty old thing. She swished her tail and waved her head with her ears back at us. To be on the safe side, we tied her up to a ring outside the loose box, so we didn't get cow kicked or nipped.

Willow was not at breakfast, and Colonel Whetton and Augusta were talking to each other gravely. The post was handed around. There was the usual missive from Mummy, mainly full of news about Hamish, the Wonder Child, and then something else with a typewritten address on the envelope and my surname spelt incorrectly as 'Crew'. I opened it and gasped. It was a ransom note!

We have Willow Vetch. We want £50,000 for her. Get the money in cash and wait for further instructions.

I leapt to my feet and rushed over to Colonel Whetton, thrusting the letter at him as if it were an unexploded bomb.

"Look! They've kidnapped Willow!" I gasped.

My words echoed around the dining-room, and after a moment of collective astonishment, the other Horsemasters were shouting questions.

"How much?" asked Bob in his pragmatic way.

"Who would think that Willow's people had that much money!" said Eustacia scornfully.

"Poor Willow!" said Dieter.

"This is a tragedy!" said Etta, who was kind-hearted to the core.

"Who on earth would think Willow is worth that much?" asked Angela.

"Gee whizz! This is like something out of the movies!" said Gerry.

"Golly gosh!" said Georgie, her eyes round in horror.

Colonel Whetton snatched up a clean napkin from the table and took the letter, then walked swiftly over to my seat and picked up the discarded envelope. Then I realised that I had put my sticky fingerprints all over it. Not only was I the last person to see Willow but the ransom note had been addressed to me. Someone must know that Willow had confided in me.

"We must call the police immediately," said Colonel Whetton.

"Having students kidnapped from Porlock Vale is a very poor show!" said Augusta, who seemed more concerned with the professional reputation of the riding school.

"Miss Crewe, when the police arrive, they will probably want to speak to you, but go now with the others and begin your riding lesson. I will ring through and get Jack Laskey to take over the session this morning," said Colonel Whetton.

Normally, the thought of Jack taking the lesson would have sent my excitement level shooting sky-high, but today I was more concerned with having to be questioned by the police. I had a dark suspicion that they might think I was somehow involved. There was the question of the dubious boyfriend and his meeting down at the pub the other night. I tried to remember his name. Willow had told me he was some sort of Eastern European royalty, which sounded extremely unlikely.

We were saddling up in the stable yard, and I cried out.

"It was Reg!"

Everyone turned around.

"What was Reg?" asked Angela sharply.

"That was the name of Willow's boyfriend. You were there, when she introduced us," I called.

"Yes, I was," said Angela. "I suppose I had better talk to the police as well."

"And Dieter, Pablo and Ariel," I said. "They saw him as well."

"Do you think it was him, that kidnapped her?" asked Angela.

"Well isn't it obvious? He was deemed unsuitable. Now he's kidnapped her for the money. Apparently, her old man is loaded," I said.

"More likely she is in cahoots with this Reg," proposed Eustacia, "and they're trying to bleed money out of her father."

"I suppose that might be possible." I hadn't wanted to think that badly of Willow, but it was a classic kidnap plot in untold narratives.

I was relieved to see that Sausage Roll had survived being kicked the day before, and he wasn't lame. Today he was being ridden by Etta, whose riding had come on by leaps and bounds. I was mounted on Treasure, and normally I would have been thrilled that Jack would see me at my best, but it seemed unimportant today.

We rode down the lane to the indoor school. Jack hurried in looking annoyed. He had probably planned a much more interesting activity for himself this morning.

"Good morning, all," he called. "This is a bit of excitement for us. Now let's put that aside for a moment and concentrate on our riding. I'm thinking some trotting with no stirrups, that will get you all in the mood!" He laughed mockingly. It crossed my mind that he wasn't the kindest man in the world, but I quickly dismissed that ignoble thought.

"Now rising trot with no stirrups, around the arena," he commanded.

I was lucky. Treasure was gorgeous to ride and lately, I'd noticed how much fitter I'd become. I could hear other Horsemasters groaning under their breath.

We trotted endlessly, changing the rein and then came the order to canter, still without stirrups.

"Now, let's do some practice at instructing. Eustacia, I want you to give the class a ten-minute lesson on . . ., Let me think." He paused, searching for inspiration.

Eustacia, who was on Sunset, rode into the centre of the arena. I noticed her smiling archly at Jack. He twinkled back at her with a glint in his eye.

"I think turns on the forehand."

Then Augusta appeared at the entrance of the arena.

"Jill Crewe, the police would like to talk to you now, and also Angela, Dieter and Pablo. Would you mind riding back to the stables and then go up to the house."

Eustacia looked a little disappointed that she'd lost half her class. I was relieved it wasn't just me. The police spoke with broad local accents, bulky in their uniforms and looking grave. These were the local police, and they were waiting for some detectives to drive over from Tavistock.

We were separated as if we might taint each other's testimonies, which was a bit late as we'd spent the morning together. If we had been intent on getting our stories straight, we would have done it by now. I was interviewed first. It was obvious that they were interested in Reg and his description, and also precisely what Willow had told me about him. I stumbled a bit when I got to the idea that he might be Eastern European royalty. I tried to describe Willow's character, as in some way, I felt that this might be the key to the mystery. I wondered if they also thought that she was colluding in her own kidnap, but they didn't suggest it, and I didn't offer it up as a possibility.

By the time we were finished, it was almost lunchtime. Augusta had rung up to say that some of the working pupils had sorted out our horses. The other Horsemasters descended on us and plied us with questions. It was the most exciting thing that had happened on the course.

They had searched Willow's room looking for clues and carried away several boxes of evidence. Angela had loitered in the passageway outside spying. She was agog with the mystery and determined to ferret out every detail.

Over lunch, there was a prevailing mood of suppressed excitement. I'm not sure that it was so much sympathy for poor Willow, possibly locked in a car boot somewhere with duct tape over her mouth, or fear that one or other of us might meet the same fate. It was more just the fizzy delight of something rather out of the ordinary occurring.

"We must do something, we can't just leave it up to the plods," said Angela in a very theatrical whisper that was so loud it positively reverberated around the room.

"Oh yes," said Oswald, who for some bizarre reason followed Angela around like a shadow.

"What are we meant to do?" sneered Eustacia, Bob nodding his head up and down beside her.

"Do you mean like investigate the mystery?" asked Etta.

"You lot have been reading too many Enid Blyton stories, who do you think you are The Famous Five?" retorted Eustacia.

"What is this Famous Five?" asked Ariel, who always seemed half a step behind the rest of us.

"Yes, if you like" snapped Angela. "Why not? In books, someone always solves the mystery."

"The police solve mysteries in real life," replied Eustacia.

For once, and it pains me to admit this, even just privately to you dear faithful readers, I was in agreement with Eustacia. I had no inclination to play the part of Jill the Super Sleuth. Willow had exasperated me from the first moment she had introduced herself. I had found her hysterical glooms and excitements ridiculous. It was as if she wanted to devour everyone around her. Very, very secretly I was glad she was gone. I was sure that she had run off with the unfortunately-named Reg and this was some sort of ruse to get money out of her rich father. I turned my mind away from it all. I was more interested in studying. It was a relief to hang out with Dieter, who seemed to feel the same way as me. I was sure that the police would not take too long to find her. Call me hard-hearted, but that is how I felt!

Angela and Oswald drew Etta into their charmed circle. After lunch, they disappeared off together, undoubtedly to begin their own private investigation. They were an unlikely trio, but I couldn't see that it would do much harm, nor much good.

Dieter and I decided to walk down to the beach to relax. It had all been rather hectic, and I wanted to recover myself. I didn't want to play silly detective games. It was then that Dieter told me. His parents had been killed some years ago. He had been only thirteen-years-old. They had been in the wrong place at the wrong time during a bank robbery, and when shots were fired, they had both caught a bullet.

"That is so sad!" I exclaimed. "That means you're an orphan!"

I think my heart went out to him because my own father had died when I was quite young. I wasn't an orphan, but I did know what it was to grow up without both parents.

"Who did you live with?"

"I had to go to my grandmother, but she died last year. She was very old. Now I live at the riding school. It is a good place. We are not exactly a family, but I do feel I belong," he said.

I felt ashamed then. I had fallen into a sort of convenient friendship with Dieter as he was such a good egg, dependable, kind and not at all egotistical. I had not really cared about him, nor asked him about himself. It wasn't even that I had been respecting his privacy, more that I didn't care enough.

By dinner time that night, the much more important detectives from Tavistock had arrived. We were all called in to be interviewed again. There were two of them, and they were playing Mr Nasty and Mr Nice. Mr Nasty had a large beetling brow and huge bushy eyebrows that met in the middle, arching over a thrusting, jutting nose. Mr Nice was smooth, suave, and completely insincere. I thought I actually preferred Mr Nasty. They were looking at me through squinted eyes, and I had an uneasy feeling that they thought I might be involved in some way. After they let me go, I went to find Dieter to tell him I was off to bed. There would be no extra study for me tonight. I was worn to a shred with all the tension.

The next morning, I received no post. Had there been anything for me, the police would have intercepted it. We were all expecting Willow's father, Bernard Vetch to arrive, sweep in with his millions and reclaim his darling daughter. Only her godmother Belinda Bliss turned up. She was a vision of utter artifice, with smartly-tailored slacks and an awful sequinned blouse. Her face was a mask of smooth foundation, huge fake eyelashes and a splash of coral-pink lipstick. I happened to be going down the passageway when she swept in the front door.

She was met by Colonel Whetton and Augusta. I heard her announcing that Mr Vetch would not be flying over from America and she was to deputise. Colonel Whetton looked around anxiously and shepherded her into a small private room and firmly shut the door.

Captain Romanski took our lesson this morning. He demanded our full attention. He could see that as a group, we were unsettled and disconsolate, and he wanted to put us back on track. I was riding Sunset.

I was utterly determined not to let her kick any other poor unfortunate horse. I didn't like her at all. Everything about her was resentful, not just bad-tempered towards other equines, but also the whole human race.

There was more about seat bones today.

"Any more instructions towards my poor bottom bones and they will crack up," muttered Georgie, who was inclined to be irreverent.

As we rode back up to the stable yard, I asked her.

"Have you heard of Willow's father, Bernard Vetch?"

"Sure," she drawled. "He's not an oilman, but he's a big manufacturer. They say he makes bombs and guns. There's a lot of money in wars."

I looked at her horrified. I was so naïve that it had never occurred to me that human beings would profit out of killing people in wars.

"We Americans, we like to get involved in other people's wars, it's good for business," she said grimacing a little. "Sometimes we supply arms to both sides, in the interest of prolonging the conflict, not exactly because of fair play."

"I can't believe it," I said shocked.

At this point, Eustacia, who had obviously been earwigging, couldn't help herself and cut in.

"Jill, you live in a ridiculous Arcadian paradise, where it's all ponies and good sportsmanship. I think it's time you grew up."

It was one of those moments when you can't possibly think of a quick retort. I stood there feeling ridiculous. I could only barely guess what an Arcadian paradise was. I imagined it was somewhere too good to be true. I would probably wake up in the dark still watches of the night with a suitable reply, but by then it would be too late.

Lunch was a rather sombre meal. Colonel Whetton, Augusta and Mrs Bliss were nowhere to be seen. No-one had any news. No sign of Willow.

After lunch Angela, Oswald and Etta took off for the village, not suggesting that anyone else go with them. They were sure to be asking around the locals to see if they could find any clues. I wondered whether they thought that Mr Vetch the Arms Dealer was offering any sort of reward.

All this excitement had taken my mind off the subject of Jack Laskey. I had to admit that even though he knew I was back at Porlock Vale, he had made no attempt to come down and see me. I might just have to face the sad fact that it had been Skydiver he was interested in, rather than my fascinating self. I thought I might walk down to the other stables and see if he were around. I would make a few last attempts to entrance him with my charms before I gave up on my romantic dream.

Ruth was in the stable yard, going around checking the hay nets and water buckets.

"Yups, Ruth!" I called. "I suppose you know all about our drama with Willow kidnapped."

"Yes, of course," she replied cheerily in her good-natured way. "Probably know more about it than you. I'm dating a member of the local constabulary!" she announced in triumph as if it were a coup of the first order. Considering the local plods who had interviewed me, I wasn't so sure it was a triumph other than love over good taste.

"Tell! Tell" I challenged her.

She dropped her voice which was usually quite hearty and loud as if talking to someone in the next field.

"The Old Man Vetch is refusing to pay up. Won't even come over."

"Oh! Poor Willow!" I said. But it made sense. Willow had the look of someone unloved. No wonder she was so neurotic. I could imagine Mummy and Richard if I got kidnapped. They'd have hotfooted it down here in a sec and would be screaming that I be rescued immediately.

"But what is going to happen? If he won't pay the ransom, do you think they will kill her?"

"Ah hah!" said Ruth, grinning at me with that I've-Got-A-Secret look.

"Tell me!" I insisted.

"They think they know where she is. There's an old lugger sitting out about six miles from the coast. It arrived a few days ago. No-one has come ashore that they know. But they have seen a small rowboat coming into a cove along the coast a-ways."

"They think Willow is in the lugger!" I cried. "But that's brilliant. They need to board the ship and rescue her."

"I guess that's the plan," said Ruth. "And my Ted is in on it. He's going with the rescue party. But you can't tell. It's all top secret. You're a journalist, aren't you?"

"You mean that piece I wrote for *Horse and Hound*. I'm not sure I'm really a journalist in the full sense of the word."

"But you know people in the press. You wrote that bit about the kids in London with the ponies?"

"How did you know that?" I asked.

"I do read *Horse and Hound,* from cover to cover. And I knew you'd come as an Equitator to write about Porlock Vale."

"Oh, of course," I said.

"You see, I think that my Ted should get the credit. He was the one who found out about the lugger. If we were at hand when they land with Willow and the kidnappers and you were to take a photo, then we could get him in the paper, and he might get promotion, you know. He wants to become a detective."

"I guess a bit of publicity at that point wouldn't hurt," I said hesitantly. Once Willow was rescued, we wouldn't be jeopardising her safety. "I do have a contact in London. She would be able to place it in the nationals. You know if Willow's father is that famous it might be of interest."

"I knew you could do something," said Ruth grinning at me. She probably had more faith in my powers than I did!

"I've got my camera. Of course. I suppose it wouldn't do any harm. When are they going to rescue her?"

"Ted isn't sure. Maybe tonight, maybe tomorrow night. They're going to approach under cover of darkness, and then they'll bring her back in the RNLI boat. They'll come into the harbour, and that's where we get the photo!"

"Alright. I agree. It would be rather a coup. I could start writing it up now, and you've got to give me Ted's full name and his part in it, and I can send it off to London. We can give a photograph to the local paper as well. I don't suppose there will be any other reporters there."

"No, of course not. It's all strictly undercover. Loose lips and all that."

"I suppose it would be. If the kidnappers got wind of it they might be off in a jiffy," I said, thinking it through. "By the way, where is Jack Laskey, is he around?" I asked.

"Oh no, he's courting the sublime godmother, Belinda, you know the woman with the unnerving look of total artificiality," said Ruth. "He's such a piece of work. He sniffs out any woman who can do him good, and Mrs Bliss is connected to some pretty rich and powerful people. You know he's got no money of his own, but he hankers after the high life. Well, you must have seen the way he sucked up to those high-faluting dressage women when you came on the Equitators' course."

At this, my heart gave an unpleasant lurch. I had begun to see the light. I had fallen out of love with a sickening plummet in my tummy. It had been Skydiver he was interested in, not me at all.

"But she's married, isn't she?" I asked.

"Married but sometimes that doesn't mean anything. She's got her hooks into Willow's father, you know. Apparently, she's got a lot of influence. And she's very keen on horses, does dressage over in America. That's the land of promise as far as Jack is concerned. Too many rich people with not enough to spend it on, but horses for him."

"Oh!" was all I managed to gasp. My mind was now running at a hundred miles an hour. Thank goodness I hadn't confided in anyone else about my tender feelings for Jack. He was Jack-the-Lad-Laskey, without a doubt, and I had been sucked in like many of the women who he had chosen to beam his radiant charm upon.

"I've got to get back. Come up to the house and tell me if it's tonight," I said. "I'll make sure I've got film in the camera, and we can go out and wait for the perfect photo opportunity."

I managed to say this in a normal voice. Inside I felt like I was cracking open, and all my passion was pouring out as if I were bleeding to death. I was plummeting to the ground after being pushed off the top of a very high building. My knees shook. Fate shrieked with malicious laughter at my past romantic hopes.

At this very moment, staggering back up the lane I saw coming towards me, none other than Mrs Belinda Bliss and Jack. They were laughing together. Obviously in cahoots over some plan that no doubt benefited each of them, but no-one else. I walked woodenly towards them, arranging my face into its most neutral expression. I felt as if all my ridiculous hopes were writ large across my forehead. They were still laughing as I got closer and perhaps unreasonably, I was sure they were laughing at me.

I returned to the main house and got my notebook and notes and went and sat in the room where we got our theory teaching.

"What's the matter, Jill?" asked Dieter, his wide brown eyes filled with concern.

"Nothing. Nothing at all," I replied. "Perhaps I'm a bit worried about Willow."

Then I chastened myself, how ignoble was that to say I cared about Willow when I was being swamped with self-pity. I began to hate myself for being so stupid. Miss Follett was talking about bandaging today. 'Bandage my heart up, having been cut to ribbons,' I thought bitterly. Although if truth were told, Jack had never indicated that he was keen on me romantically. It had all been my stupid, ridiculous fantasies. It was a classic schoolgirl thing, and I couldn't believe that I had fallen into that trap.

I remembered then how Ann had been duped by the romantic Pierre, who had been playing her while he cavorted secretly with another woman. She had been in the depths of depression when it had all come out. But at least that had been a real romance. She had been staying with his family, introduced as the girl he was about to propose to. She really had been made a fool of. I had not, only in my mind. That was bad enough! I decided then and there, to never entertain any tender thought, until my swain was down on his knees in front of me proposing with a diamond engagement ring in his hand!

I began to make some notes on the side of my book, in shorthand and code, about the sort of story that I could write about Willow's abduction. In terms of my journalistic hopes, this was surely a coup. Vaguely I wondered if I should go off to a war zone to be a foreign correspondent. That was what men did when their hearts were broken, run away and join the Foreign Legion. The only war that I knew of at that moment was the Vietnam War, and somehow, I imagined there might be very smelly swamps and mosquitos and piles of dead bodies to photograph. I decided that that wasn't really me.

Ruth was as good as her word. I came out of the dining room after our evening meal, and she was loitering in the passageway. I hurried over to her, and she told me it was on. They were setting off at midnight that night. I arranged to meet her down in the lane at one in the morning. There would undoubtedly be an uncomfortable wait for them to come in and some anxious moments hoping for the best, but it would be worth it to get the news photograph of the year with Willow stepping ashore to safety. Or perhaps they might be carrying her in a body bag. I shuddered at the thought. But if I were ever to be a foreign war correspondent, I needed to toughen up.

I forced myself to sit with Dieter in the library. We went over our notes on bandaging, and then there was rugging, and pulling manes and tails. It was perhaps not the most fascinating topic in our curriculum, but they were all-important issues. Dieter gave me a few searching glances, but I carried on as best I could.

I went up to bed early and tried to sleep for a couple of hours with my alarm clock set for twelve-thirty. I had laid out some warm clothes, my camera loaded with film and some savoury biscuits with cheese from the sideboard that I had stuffed in my pocket. I wished I could have a flask of warm milky tea but couldn't go down and ask in the kitchen. It would provoke too many questions. Perhaps a tough, cynical war correspondent would have a flask of brandy.

I couldn't sleep for ages, until finally at midnight, I fell asleep for what seemed like just one minute and then the alarm was ringing. I hauled myself out of bed. Creeping down the corridor, I quietly let myself out of the side door. I made my way down to the road by the light of the silvery moon. It felt like I was in boarding school on a schoolgirl adventure in the middle of the night. The wind whistled through the treetops above me. I could smell the sea, beckoning me to witness the dramatic event that was going to make me famous in the journalistic world. My Better Self poked its head up, and I hoped that Willow would be returned to us safely and in one piece, with no fingers cut off.

It suddenly dawned on me that this wasn't a jolly jape. It seemed that Willow really had been kidnapped and was in the hands of a ruthless bunch of ruffians who were holding her on an old lugger, probably leaking like a sieve and threatening to fall into the black sea and drown them all.

Ruth loomed at me out of the dark.

"Come on, Jill" she hissed. "I thought you weren't coming."

"I'm ready for the off," I said, adopting some idiom that seemed suitable for our adventure.

"You've got the camera," she said roughly. For her, the most important thing was to get her chap in the papers.

"Yes, with full film loaded and a spare in my pocket," I whispered back, thinking it sounded like a loaded gun. We crept down the lane. The moon gave an eerie silvery light and threw strange shadows across the road.

"Do you think the kidnappers will see the police approaching?" I asked.

"They couldn't wait for less moonlight. Every hour that poor Willow is captured puts her more at risk," said Ruth, obviously well-versed in the thinking of the police.

We got to the village and Ruth led me down the back lanes, and we came out at the harbour.

"There's quite a few narrow footpaths between the houses, the ways the smugglers used in the olden days," she whispered.

The moonlight playing across the smooth sand of the beach was suddenly obscured. Black clouds rolled in from the sea, and the landscape darkened ominously. Then a deep rumble and cracks of lightning on the horizon and the rain came down like someone was emptying buckets of water on us.

We scurried to the fallen-down pier and tried to shelter under it. But the rain poured through the old planks above us which were weather-worn and decaying. I wished I had brought my mac, but somehow such a humdrum item of clothing hadn't seemed suitable. Anyway, one needed an oilskin to keep sheltered from this drenching rain.

"At least the kidnappers won't see the police boat approaching," hissed Ruth in a stage whisper.

I was beginning to hate this. Rain was seeping in an unpleasant snail trail down my collar and back. It was dark and bitterly cold. I began to wonder what on earth I was doing here. Waiting on a beach for a photograph for a story that just might, but probably wouldn't, be emblazoned across the front pages of the local rag, and might be hidden in the middle of a London newspaper. I wished we had a flask of something hot to drink. Instead, I produced the crackers and cheese, and we munched.

The hours seemed to stretch into eternity. I feared that no-one would arrive, the sun would not rise, and I would never sleep in a warm, comfortable bed again. Cold was washing through me when I should have been alert and vibrating with the expectation of a scoop. I was terribly disappointed with myself.

Finally, the boat appeared. The noise of the storm and the waves had masked the sound of the outboard. People spilled onto the beach in front of us, but it was dark and not at all suitable for the photograph of the century. How had I not thought of this? There was no helpful spotlight lighting up the characters in this drama, as if they were on a stage. Ruth couldn't help herself. She ran forward to find out what was happening. The clouds parted for a moment, and I could see three men in handcuffs guarded by three burly police officers. In a bundle of blankets was a bedraggled Willow. Her hair looked more unkempt than ever.

Her weird googly eyes were swivelling. But she was alive! I had to re-mind myself that this was the main point.

Then there was a Land Rover driving across the sand with its head-lights on full beam. This was my chance. I held up the camera and began to click wildly. A whole film and at least one frame would be enough to hang the story upon. Out of the Land Rover leapt Jack and Be-linda. They looked well-groomed, neat and poised in contrast to those who were struggling up the beach. This would be the photograph that would sell the story!

One of the policemen began to stride towards me.

"Who are you? What are you doing?"

"I'm Willow's friend," I declared, perhaps stretching the truth a little. "I've come down to see if she is safe."

"Hmmmph," he grunted disapprovingly. "Had to take a photo for that, I suppose?"

"Sorry" I said, stuffing the camera in my satchel. "Where are you taking Willow? Is she coming back with us to Porlock Vale?"

"That's for her guardian, Mrs Bliss," he said cocking his head to-wards the older woman who now had her arm around Willow.

"I'm so glad she is safe," I gushed, hoping desperately he wasn't going to confiscate my camera and the film.

By now the raggedy group had made their way up to the road. The police station was just a street away.

"Run along home, now," said the policeman. "We've got things to do, and your sort just gets in the way."

"Do you know who the kidnappers are?" I asked cheekily. I was bouncing back into my role as Jill the Intrepid Journalist.

"You'll find out in good time, now scram kid!"

Ruth had also been summarily told to go home, so the two of us walked back up the hill to Porlock Vale.

"At least they rescued her. I had wondered if she wasn't in on the plan. You know to run away with the boyfriend and get the dough out of her father," I mused.

"That's what the police thought too, but that's just between me, you and the gatepost," said Ruth.

"Did Ted tell you anything? Were there guns or stuff like that? Knives?"

"No, it was pretty easy. They were asleep, and they just leapt upon them, and it was all over in a trice," said Ruth who had managed a few words with him before she had been told to get lost.

"I hope some of the photos came out," I said.

"Yes, I do want Ted to get some of the glory," said Ruth, smiling into the darkness.

"Thank goodness Jack and that Yank woman turned up with the headlights or we wouldn't have got photos at all," I said.

"I'll take them down to the chemist today. I've got a half-day. I'll ask them to do a rush job on them," said Ruth.

"Good idea," I said. Suddenly, it was terribly important that the photos came out. Without them, any story was going to be a non-event.

By breakfast, everyone at Porlock Vale knew what had happened in the night. The table was abuzz with speculation and 'ooohs' and 'ahhhs'. I didn't want to admit I'd been on the scene. It would make me look like a thruster. I was just one of the group of students this morning, absolutely starving after the events of the night. I heaped up my plate and ate. Then I felt so exhausted I just wanted to crawl into bed for the day. But onward and upward, I went down to the stable yard with the others and saddled up for another rigorous training session.

At lunchtime, Jack and Mrs Bliss swanned in. Everyone clamoured to hear the news.

"Dear Willow is up in her room resting after her terrible ordeal," said Mrs Bliss.

Immediately I made plans to sneak up there and see what I could get out of Willow that could be quoted in the story.

"The kidnappers have all been charged, and they've been taken to Tavistock for further questioning," said Jack, as if he were solely responsible for their apprehension.

"Thanks to you, Jack," said Mrs Bliss fawningly.

My dark suspicions about their burgeoning relationship were confirmed. She was married! How naïve was I! Rich, American, passionate about horses! What more could Jack be looking for, and it wasn't as if he wanted to tie himself down.

I imagined her whisking him back to America to showcase to all her envious friends. He could bedazzle them with his British charms, and undoubtedly, he would have his pick of American horses and heiresses! As you will see, I wasn't too far off the mark, but I had underestimated Jack. He was a lounge lizard extraordinaire. He wanted to secure himself a position in American society so he couldn't be dropped like a cold potato when he was no longer a novelty.

After lunch, I crept up to Willow's bedroom. The curtains were drawn, and her pale face was half-hidden by blankets.

"Ohhh!" she cried with a thin wail as I crept in.

"Shhhh, shhhh, it's only me Jill. You're safe now." I hoped I hadn't frightened her out of her wits, which were pretty shaky even before this all happened.

"Oh, Jill," she sighed.

I went and sat on the bed and wondered if I should take her hand to comfort her, but I couldn't quite manage that degree of play-acting.

"Are you alright?" I asked.

"Yes, no, I don't think so," she said in a thin, miserable voice that seemed to slur over her words. They had probably given her tranquilisers.

"What on earth happened? Was it your boyfriend? Was he mixed up in this?"

"It wasn't Reg's fault, he confided in a friend, and he said he would help us to escape, but then it all went wrong, and really his friend just wanted to make money out of my father. But my father wouldn't pay, and things got pretty nasty!"

Poor old Willow, talk about a double whammy! What sort of a father would do that?

"So are you and Reg going to be able to stay together? Perhaps your father might change his mind?" I suggested.

"No Belinda has put the skids under him. She wants him charged as well. It doesn't matter what I say," said Willow looking utterly woebegone.

There was a discrete knock at the door, and Jack peeped around the corner.

"Oh, Jack!" exclaimed Willow. "Belinda told me you would be coming to make sure I was alright."

He slid into the room like a panther and went to the other side of the bed. He took Willow's pale claw that was resting on top of the coverlet.

"Dear Willow! Are you feeling better?" he asked in what I hoped was a paternal manner. But perhaps not?

"I'm much better," she sniffled. "But I want to go home. I don't really like it here. Belinda said you would come with us. So we can explain everything to Daddy."

"You're going to America!" I said accusingly to Jack.

He looked over at me as if he hadn't even noticed that I was there.

"Jill, surely there's somewhere you could be. Willow and I want to spend some time together."

I looked at him aghast. Willow simpered. Mrs Bliss, Yes! I could imagine him working his charm. But to do that to Willow seemed so cruel. I said nothing and then leapt up and rushed out. I was feeling sick. I thought I might throw up.

I went down to the stable yard. Somehow the presence of horses, particularly my lovely, stolid Sausage Roll was reassuring, wholesome and good! I went into his loose box and patted his thick neck, feeling his warmth and smooth coat. I had had a vision of the future. Jack and Willow walking down the aisle, with Belinda, a matron of honour looking on, smiling a secret smile. It would all be organised to her advantage. What a wicked world of adult machinations!

The police wanted Willow to stick around so she could give evidence against the kidnappers, but Belinda was determined that they should fly back to America. She insisted that Willow could return to England when the wheels of justice, which did sometimes grind exceedingly slow, got to the actual trial. We all piled out to the front of the house as Mrs Bliss had a chauffeur-driven Rolls drive up. Willow took her suitcases, Belinda had a pile of very expensive luggage, and Jack took a rather smart leather bag. Presumably, he would be showered with new clothes upon his arrival. He and Willow were to be married!

We all wished them well. The blokes patted Jack on the back. We girls kissed her and looked into her goggling eyes and told her how lucky she was. They drove away.

"Well, doesn't that take the cake!" exclaimed Angela and we all agreed. There seemed no need for discussion, as a group we were of one mind.

"Looks like we're down an instructor," said Eustacia. I wondered if she might put herself forward as a possible replacement.

My photos came back from the chemist, and there was one rather good one of the group, on the beach. Willow was standing, bedraggled, wrapped in a blanket and two of the kidnappers were in handcuffs under the stern eye of Ted. I looked through some other snaps I had taken and saw that at one point I had managed to capture Mrs Bliss and Jack looking at each other as if they were a pair of cats drinking from the same saucer of cream. A quite wicked thought popped into my mind. Now, it's not that I wanted to be a muck-raker, but there was a story here that might well sell in America, and I definitely had the contact to place it there. I rang Hetty and blurted it out.

"Oh well done, Jill!" she said. "I'll do the background on Bernie Vetch, that name certainly rings a bell, and with your photos and your account of the kidnap, it will be a beaut. Of course, the Belinda and Jack in cahoots angle makes it all the more salacious, just what the reading public is after. This should pay your fees for that course."

I didn't feel quite right about it. One day I hoped to write in such a way that I might be described as someone with a 'rapier brain' who worked for the good of the world through the Fourth Estate, which is the power of journalism. On the other hand, I thought that Mrs Bliss and Jack deserved it and Willow was probably too wet and bedraggled to bother to read a magazine. I felt as if I had to in some way get pay-back for all that wasted emotion on imagining myself as Mrs Laskey. I find it almost impossible just to write those words. I can't believe that I had ever been so stupid!

The story got sent off, and the magazine paid for it. It was only just published, and then Jack F. Kennedy was assassinated, and every-thing else that was in any way newsworthy got swamped. So, no-one was ever really going to be interested, but I had the bucks in the bank, or rather a nice fat cheque posted to me from Hetty. I did feel a bit grubby and swore to myself that never again would I chase a salacious story. I would follow the narrow and righteous path of dressage com-petitions and worthy competitors who had interesting, but wholesome lives. Which just goes to show how naïve I was!

The humdrum matter of finishing my course, sitting up late at night with Dieter revising stable management and veterinary care, the nerve-wracking sit-down exam, the riding exam and demonstrating instruc-tors' skills went on. I sank myself in all the honest toil and serious study. We all got our certificates, even little Etta whose riding had come on no end. I was now QUALIFIED! Somehow the Willow incident had led us all to band together, and on our last day, we swapped addresses and swore to become lifelong friends – even Eustacia and bumptious Bob Nutley. Gerry had invited me to Texas, and Dieter had invited me to Germany. In a fit of enthusiasm, I declared that everyone should come to the castle for a reunion next summer.

It was all planned that I should set off for Essex in my horse box, then I would swing by Pool Cottage before I began the long drive back to Scotland. Linda had written and explained that she just couldn't manage to get Skydiver to any competitions, but he was doing well, as fit as a fiddle, jumped like an expert and she was sure that I would be storming around the horse trials in the spring. Life was looking pretty good! It would be hard to decide what to do next!

JILL BOOKS

Jill Rides Cross Country (Jill Series Book 1)

Jill Has Two Horses (Jill Series Book 2)

Jill Goes Pony Trekking (Jill Series Book 3)

Jill and the Mystery of the Missing Horse (Jill Pocket Books)

Jill and the Steeplechaser (Jill Series Book 4)

Jill Dreams of a Dressage Horse (Jill Series Book 5)

Jill and the Horsemasters (Jill Series Book 6)

All Change at Blainstock Stables (Jill Pocket Books)

CPSIA information can be obtained
at www.ICGtesting.com
Printed in the USA
BVHW091425031220
594765BV00010B/1357